Contents

For Brian

FOREWORD

" A handful of periwinkles to make kitchen"

Lady Gregory, *The Workhouse Ward.*

HAD I WRITTEN THIS SMALL TRIBUTE to Irish shellfish in the Irish language it might have been called *cnuasach mara*. That is the name – it means "sea pickings" – given to the eclectic mixture of shellfish and seaweed that was traditionally gathered on Irish shores for human consumption. "Kitchen" is the vernacular word for it in Hiberno-English. That is what this book is: an eclectic gathering of some of the known facts, the old legends and the very real modern stories of how we have utilized our precious shellfish resource down through our history and how we are now cultivating and managing it. There is little enough here that will be entirely new for everyone. But I hope that some readers will be entertained even if they are not enlightened and others will be enlightened if only in a whimsical way. Each chapter stands largely on its own and may be dipped into as the reader wishes. Hopefully all will find pleasure somewhere in the text or in the pictures without too much difficulty.

The Irish shellfisheries have changed almost beyond recognition in the last quarter of a century. Some will remember how we moved from local harvesting, often by hand or by small rowing boat, to the present state of mechanical harvesting and developed aquaculture. They will need no reminding of the aching backs, sunburned heads, chafed hands and bruised limbs of those changing days. Nor of the cold fallings-in; the hot fallings-out; the concerns over tide marks and exam marks; the long beards and short tempers; the ropes, the rafts, the buoys, the buckets, the bags and the other paraphernalia that were so often in short supply; the loans, the banks, the bureaucracy and the stormy nights that were longer and more trying. How could they ever forget the joy of a first successful settlement, a first good spatfall, a first harvest? Or the pleasure of wrapping frozen hands around a hot whiskey or buying the first (second-hand) van? What could compare with clean dry socks and a new pair of wellies, or a pet day in Connemara, or working outdoors on a clear day, or just being your own boss? These memories are still too new and the *dramatis personae* still sufficiently active and healthy to make a full telling of their story premature, even perhaps risky, for the person who has the temerity to make the attempt. Therefore this *cnuasach* concentrates on the broad social and biological framework within which their story unfolds. Like the old-fashioned dredge, it barely scratches the surface, skipping from item to item hopefully doing little damage while still gleaning a worthwhile catch.

There really is only one true test of the merit of a food resource and that is to try it out at the table. That is why I give some recipes and mention some good eating-places, where shellfish are likely to be served sympathetically, and in some blessed cases, *con amore*. Few will be disappointed if they "have a go" at the species mentioned, especially when prepared by one of our very talented chefs. Our Continental visitors will need no introduction to the pleasures of Irish seafood. They will already be familiar with it from its presence on the fish markets and gourmet tables of Europe. It is we ourselves who need to overcome the idea that fish and shellfish are some form of penitential food. True, many of us can still remember times when religious observance decreed that fish alone could be eaten on certain days of the week and during certain periods of the year. Red meat in those times was thought to inflame the passions; seafood was regarded as conducive to a gentler disposition. There is little doubt that shellfish rest gently on the stomach: Pliny tells us that *". . . [Palourdes] do mollify and soften the bellie . . . the bladder is cleansed by a diet of scallops . . . and clams relax the bowel"*. To what delightful extent they may or may not inflame the passions is a personal matter best left to the individual (or couple, preferably) to research as often and as thoroughly as is seemly.

Sometimes our reluctance to enjoy shellfish results from an excess of squeamishness. While this is understandable when they are eaten live there is no reason to demur when they are cooked. And while there may once have been a small danger that uncooked shellfish from some places might be "suspect", today our production techniques, our constant vigilance in monitoring the water and our health and safety regulations ensure that this danger is extremely small. The burgeoning world market for shellfish indicates that it is now unquestionably "cool" food, recommended by culinary and medical experts as part of a healthy diet.

Irish shellfish have come a long way from the time when they were regarded as *bia bocht* – food for the poor. This good news story is not yet near its end. Indeed it is only now that our shellfish output is attaining the real prominence its prime quality warrants. This book is intended to celebrate the work of the fishermen, the researchers, the shellfish farmers, the chefs and the agencies that are bringing this about. *Bon appetit*!

Chapter 1
IRELAND AND THE SEA

[The sea . . .]. Its teeming womb was our store-room. When sick we smelt its breath and chewed the grasses off its stranded bottoms, and were reconditioned in our health. When sad, we sat and listened to its moaning and lost our sorrow. It was our common mother as well as the father of our strength and knowledge.

Liam O'Flaherty, *Two Years,* 1930.

IT'S A LONG ROAD, we are told, that has no turning. And what a good thing that is, especially when the road is an Irish boreen winding its uneven, erratic, thorn-shrouded way to the sea. (Fig. 1). When at last it makes its final turn to reveal the water, whose presence will have been signalled long before by the aqueous quality of the light, we experience one of the great pleasures of island life. The thrill of coming face to face with the timeless restlessness of the sea, whether in sheltered coves or in the great exposure of an open Atlantic shore, is never quite the same on any two occasions or in any two places. The sights, the smells, the sounds, the very feel of the air all combine to make each occasion distinct, each experience new, each visit unique.

Ireland's long and indented coastline extends to an impressive 7,000 kilometres, yet no place in the whole country is more than 100 kilometres from the coast. Fortunately we are blessed with numerous roads, large and small, so that the thrill of the sea is never far away. We have, for example, over 87,000 kilometres of regional and local roads, more than 25 kilometres per 1,000 population, which is five times the norm in the rest of the European Union. But at a finer level, the country is criss-crossed by thousands of kilometres of even smaller boreens, so that the network of communication throughout the island reaches truly fantastic proportions. Boreens (*boithrín* in Irish, meaning a small

Fig. 1. An Irish boreen winding its way to the sea.

road) are the small, narrow, usually unmetalled roads, sometimes hardly more than tracks, which weave a seemingly erratic course through the countryside. They are the ancient work routes of the indigenous population, etched into the land by the feet of man and of his beasts rather than by man's hands or by his design. They are very common in the coastal counties where many of them lead to the seashore. Their abundance here is no chance matter either. They testify to the importance that access to the sea has had throughout our history since the first Irish people set up home in the northeast of the island about 7,000 years ago. These original inhabitants built their fragile stake-and-wattle homes beside the shore and lived out their lives entirely by the sea. Only in later generations did they migrate inland, but not before they had worked their way down the coast from the Northeast to the very Southwest. Here, on the outermost periphery of Europe – its *ne plus ultra* – the original Irish traversed the rugged margin of their island home before venturing inland up the courses of its great rivers. In that long colonizing expansion they, and those who came after them, left clear evidence of their intimate dependence on the sea and the resources it provided.

Middens, huge heaps of discarded shells and occasional bones, the remains of their fishing, foraging and hunting activities, mark the sites of their occupation. At Dunloughan Bay near Ballyconneely in County Galway such middens, dating from the Bronze Age to the tenth century A.D., are being exposed by erosion and over-grazing. It has been suggested that they will have eroded away entirely within the next quarter of a century. Until then, they give a wonderful snap-shot of early habitation sites in the west of Ireland. Close by the ruined stone foundations of pre-mediaeval houses (Fig 2), the middens contain rich deposits of oysters, cockles, limpets, winkles, dog whelks and razorfish interspersed with burned stones and wickerwork reduced to charcoal. Oysters seem to dominate the earlier Bronze Age sites, winkles and limpets the later sites. Some of these species are still, to this day, among the most important species that we are harvesting, cultivating and consuming to a greater degree than ever before. But to see them at Dunloughan, False and Mannin Bays, graphic and poignant confirmation of our early and long-continued dependence on our shellfish resources is an experience not to be missed, especially in the company of an enthusiastic archaeologist.

When the early people moved inland they did not lose complete contact with the coast. The Irish never, in fact, fully lost their interest in the sea and in sea life. The lacework of coastal boreens in the maritime counties is not the only legacy and proof of this abiding interest. The majority of our population has always lived in coastal areas, as we still do today, and our largest, most important towns and cities have always been on the coast.

Even a cursory glance at the map indicates the tattered, fragmented nature of Ireland's coastline especially along the western seaboard (Fig. 3). Better still, a walk or drive along the coast emphasises the labyrinthine nature of the land and seascape. Headlands, islands, inlets, creeks, bays, saleens, estuaries, sandbanks,

Inset is a picture of the shells exposed at another site in this locality. It includes oysters, razor shells, winkles and limpets. The dark arc in the bottom right is an area of charcoal from a piece of burned wickerwork.

Fig. 2. Outline of a stone house and small enclosure dating from about the eighth to the tenth century A.D. This is a settlement site at Dunloughan, near Mannin Bay in County Galway. Other sites in this locality have been dated to the Bronze Age. To the right and on the ridge in the middle distance there are exposed shell middens.

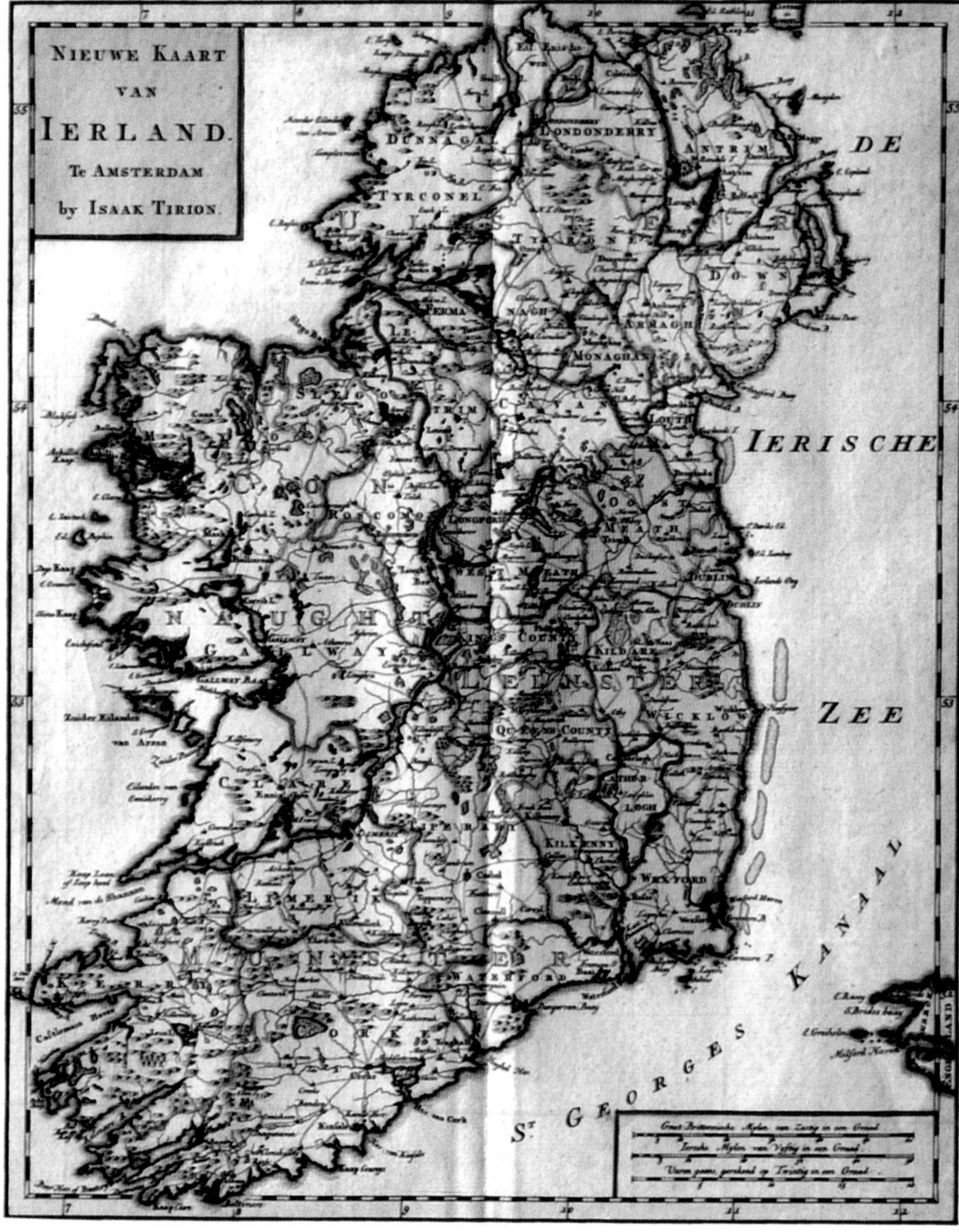

Fig. 3. Map of Ireland published in 1754 by Isaak Tirion of Amsterdam. The south, west and north coasts are ragged and indented. The shellfish beds lie within the bays and inlets on these coasts. On the east coast the great banks that held huge stocks of oysters, mussels, razorfish and whelks are clearly shown lying offshore from counties Louth, Wicklow and Wexford.

mudflats, rocks, reefs, beaches and cliffs contribute to a tapestry that is unlike anything found inland. Life in this kaleidoscopic, transitional zone induces in the coastal dweller a mind-set almost alien to that of the landsman. Tidal, diurnal and seasonal rhythms are somehow more pronounced and better paced in the marginal places where land meets water. Sounds, too, carry better over water and the light lingers longer. To the coast dweller, the sea is not what separates two pieces of land but what joins them. This is easy to understand since in many ways the sea is easier to traverse, especially with a heavy load, than the rocky road. It is often the "short cut" from one headland neighbour to another. Heinrich Becker's *"I mBéal na Farraige"* recounts, in the people's own words, just how easily and naturally the men and women of Aran and Connemara moved from land into water and back again in their seaweed gathering and shellfish harvesting activities, as if there were no change of medium, no wet and dry, no land and sea. Land boundaries extended invisibly into the sea and the shore was often a patchwork of informal, family-held plots as diverse as those on dry land. Rights to seaweed and shellfish within such plots were jealously guarded and highly valued. To this day, standing stones on many shores mark the limits of ancient littoral plots now long abandoned and sometimes forgotten.

Fig. 4. The tattered and fragmented coastline of the west of Ireland.

But the Irish, it is sometimes said, have little or no history of exploiting the sea and have no long tradition of sea fishing or maritime exploration to rival those of our European partners. We do not even behave like an island people. For instance, our officially recorded annual *per capita* consumption of fish and shellfish, 16 kg in 2001, is only two thirds of the EU average and has consistently been one of the lowest in Europe until very recent times. And, until our entry to the European Community, we made no trenchant claims to ownership of, or even any direct stewardship interest in, our offshore marine environment.

I believe this view to be incomplete. It reflects a fundamental misunderstanding of the geographic location of Ireland, the nature of its coastline (Fig. 4) and the way in which we have traditionally harvested our marine resources. To sail away from the coast, far out into the deep Atlantic was not, until relatively recent historical times, an experience to be wished for or a hazard to be undertaken lightly. The great European maritime expansion to the West did not get properly underway until the late 15th century, so dangerous and daunting was the open Atlantic Ocean perceived to be. We sometimes forget that to cross even the usually calm Irish Sea required considerable courage and skill until the nineteenth century. And, even today, the largest ferry ships with all their navigational and propulsion aids cannot set sail in all weathers on that short, relatively easy crossing. Is it any wonder then that mediaeval Ireland, facing the great Atlantic void and knowing from experience the fury of its storms, did not seek to probe the threatening vastness of its offshore deeps? Nor was there ever cause to venture very far from a shore that abounded with all the resources needed to supplement what the land provided. And what a diversity of resources that was – food fish, of course, and shellfish, seaweed for manure and medicine, sharks and cetaceans for oil, birds and their eggs, sand and shell for floor covering or soil lightening and stones for building and boundary walls.

In addition, who could foretell what wondrous items of flotsam and jetsam might not be thrown up by a great storm, what bounteous new Armada treasures might not once again fortuitously enrich the coast? From the earliest times there were elaborate rules governing the valuable rights to flotsam and jetsam, laid down in the ancient Irish law text of sea-judgements called *Muirbhretha*. Even the early Irish saints were well acquainted with the shore and its gifts. St. Patrick, as we shall see, owed his life to a topshell; St. Columcille was a veritable beach-comber; and we can easily imagine a young St. Brendan standing on a Kerry beach examining the tropical seeds, stems and leaves that are still regularly washed ashore, wondering what lands, what peoples lay beyond the western horizon to whom he might bring the faith (Fig. 5). He eventually undertook his great westward voyage of exploration and adventure, recorded in the *Navigatio Sancti Brendani*. The strange marvels, fabulous events and frightening happenings he recounted may well have influenced later generations from venturing after him into that fearful and awesome unknown. As the early maps warned ominously on their margins *". . . here be sea monsters!"*

Fig. 5. The early Irish monks regarded the sea as a desert, a place to be alone with God and away from the world of man. This sculpture near Cahirciveen, commissioned by Kerry County Council in 1995, is by Eamon O'Doherty and is entitled To the Skelligs. *It seems to capture the simplicity and starkness of the vision of the monks as they removed themselves to that most austerely spiritual of places,* Sceilig Mhichíl, *a barren, lonely rock off the Kerry coast.*

The early Irish, then, had no reason or need to seek sustenance or resource from the deep ocean. The abundance of the shore and inshore waters was more than sufficient for them. Foremost among their sea harvest were the many species of shellfish that could be picked by hand or gathered using small boats. The number, the ages and the extent of shell middens dotted all around the coast are sure evidence of the importance of shellfish in the domestic economy of Ireland from the very beginning. Indeed, so important were shellfish that they are mentioned in the very earliest written historical records that are still extant, legal tracts dating from the seventh and eighth centuries. Both before and after the Norman Conquest, for example, shellfisheries were inscribed in legislation governing the community of Dublin, long before that settlement rejoiced in the title "City", not to say "Capital City". But the oldest record of all is that preserved in the sedimentary rocks that make up so much of our country. Our limestone bedrock is rich in fossil shells that lived more than three hundred million years ago, when Ireland itself was being formed in an ancient sea. These bivalves might have remained forever unseen and unknown, locked in their ancient, stoney bed. But when limestone rock is cut and used for building they are exposed again to our gaze and we can only wonder at the abundance and persistence of these creatures that are so much older than man himself. Their fossils certainly impart a quality of age and permanence even to the most modern buildings (Fig. 6).

Fig. 6. The oldest record of shellfish in Ireland is in the fossil record. Much of Ireland's limestone was laid down in the seas of the Carboniferous period, about 400 million years ago. Here the Carboniferous shells are exposed once again in a cut limestone block in the wall of Galway Cathedral, adding a quality of antiquity to a very recent building.

The first written records refer specifically to limpets and periwinkles and to the prohibition on gathering seafood on Sundays. By the thirteenth century cockles and mussels were firmly embedded in the laws and the diet of Dubliners and oysters gradually made their appearance later on. Urban populations, here and elsewhere, always seem to have favoured bivalve molluscs above the humbler gastropods, whereas rural communities remained faithful for a longer period to the humbler sorts. There can however be little doubt that shellfish, of whatever dress, formed a valued component of the diet of rich and poor throughout all of our history.

Although greatly increased in popularity of late, shellfish are not to everyone's taste. *Chacun son goût*! Even shellfish themselves are allowed to be "picky" like this about what they will and will not eat and almost all the species we are concerned with are strictly vegetarian with extremely fastidious tastes. They constitute two main classes within the phylum or group of animals we call Molluscs. One class – the bivalves – are so called because they have two valves, or pieces, to their shell. The oysters, mussels, cockles, clams, razorfish and scallops belong to this group. The second class is called the gastropod class, because their digestive system and their foot form a single mass. They have only one piece to their shell and are rather like the common land snails we see everywhere. This group includes the winkles, whelks, limpets and abalones.

Bivalves feed by drawing a current of water inside the shell and over very large filtering surfaces called the gills. These are nature's own sifting conveyor belts. They are covered in millions of tiny projections called cilia that all beat in the general direction of the mouth. The inhaled water carries all sorts of planktonic food in the form of micro-algae and tiny animals. As the water passes through the gills the particles it carries are deposited onto the gill surface. The synchronous beating of the cilia wafts the particles towards the mouth and only those of exactly the right size and composition make it all the way. Particles that are not of the correct type are sifted off the gill and rejected. Just before the mouth a pair of palps runs a final check on the items arriving from the gills ensuring that only the desired food will enter the holy of holies! All the rejected particles are swept out of the shell chamber – spat out, in plain terms. This is indeed a very effective winnowing system. The volume of water that the bivalves filter in this manner is enormous and we call them "filter feeders" because of this. All of the water in Galway Bay – about 12 million, million litres – passes through filter feeding organisms each year in this way.

The gastropods avoid the problem of processing vast quantities of water by feeding in an entirely different manner. They creep about on rocks and on seaweeds, eating micro-algae as they go (Fig 7). This is just the way cattle and sheep feed on land so we call the gastropods "grazers" for that reason. They have a wonderful sort of tongue called a *radula,* which is like a rasping file. It enables them to scrape the algae off the surface of rocks and larger seaweeds with great efficiency. Naturally, they select precisely the kinds of algae they will eat and, like the bivalves, they only consume what suits them. So we can see that shellfish do not eat any old food, but choose carefully what they take into the stomach. This, of course, is why they themselves are so deliciously delicate and why we can so often eat them uncooked. While it can pay for an animal to be "picky" in this way it has its drawbacks, too. If the chosen food items are in short supply, as they sometimes can be, life can be tough for a while. Indeed, in some bays in France the number of shellfish that can be grown is now limited because there are not sufficient suitable food items in the plankton to support the vast numbers of shellfish under cultivation. We do not have this problem in Ireland – yet.

Up to the nineteenth century it was mainly the poor who gathered shellfish for consumption locally. Such fare, called *cnuasach mara,* ("sea pickings" is one translation) was known as *bia bocht,* or poor food. For this reason, shellfish failed to appear in the written accounts of commerce (and taxation!) leading some commentators to conclude that they were not eaten here at all. Thereby arose the myth that the Irish have no marine food tradition. Things that are common or ordinary tend to be overlooked by "History" and the gathering of simple seafood leaves almost no footprint on "History's" pages. But we know that absence of evidence is not evidence of absence and what information we do have, from archaeological digs, ancient writings and travellers' accounts, confirms that good use was made of shellfish in Ireland especially in times of hardship. The same is true for British shellfish and probably those of our other European neighbours as well.

When we look in later chapters at the way in which our shellfish resources have been utilized over time we will see that it falls into four distinct phases. The first is the gathering/harvesting phase in which the animals are gathered predominantly for the collector's own use and that of his family and neighbours. Gathering is then rarely excessive, often seasonal, usually localized and makes little demand on the standing stock. Once any shellfish species becomes a traded commodity it enters the second phase, that of exploitation. In this, the species is exploited for sale rather than harvested for personal use. Catches are larger and determined by price and commercial demand; seasons are often ignored; the fishery spreads out; "professional" fishermen enter the fishery and control passes effectively to commercial interests through price and demand mechanisms. The inevitable outcome of the exploitation phase is over-exploitation, resulting in the eventual depletion of the wild stocks. This, of course, does not go unnoticed and some people come to realize the need for sensible management of the resource if it is not to become entirely exhausted. This realization may initiate the third phase, that of resource management, which involves elements of mandatory catch or effort control, habitat protection, environmental enhancement and other actions. Many of these activities are beyond the capacity of the individual fisherman on his own and it is here that the help of professional support agencies like the Marine Institute and An Bórd Iascaigh Mhara (BIM) becomes essential. Through such agencies scientific, technical, marketing and management advice and support are made available, together with assistance in the matter of increasingly important health and safety regulations.

But even the best management cannot develop a wild indigenous biological resource like shellfish beyond a certain level; further progress may require a final phase, that of cultivation, or aquaculture *sensu stricto*. For instance, it may be necessary to introduce new stock from elsewhere, or a completely new species, or to construct a hatchery and rearing facilities to overcome the shortages of wild spat and the problem of the early mortalities associated with juvenile life in the wild.

All species seem to go through the general phases outlined, but not all at the same time or at the same rate. This book recounts the stories of the various species as they transit from local harvesting to modern cultivation. For all of them, the gathering phase lasted well into the late eighteenth century. Transport conditions before then simply were not suitable to carry live sea creatures safely to distant markets, so gathering remained largely for local use and trade was slow to develop. The oyster was the first Irish shellfish species to enter the exploitation phase. Over-exploitation soon followed, triggered partly by the excessive demand that resulted from the growth of the cities and the expansion of rapid rail transportation in the first half of the nineteenth century. Other species only commenced to make a significant appearance in the records when they entered trade and commerce in a major way, as they started to do from about the mid-nineteenth century on. In fact, with the exception of oysters whose heyday was the mid-nineteenth century and periwinkles, most Irish shellfish have seriously entered the arena of trade only in the last thirty years or so. Many shellfish appearing on European markets as "new" species are, in fact, ones that have been known and harvested locally for generations but that have only lately been presented to the wider public. In terms of the provision of food, they have changed from being harvested – a sustainable activity – to being exploited, a sure recipe for ultimate extinction. Unless, that is, we succeed in harnessing good management and best aquaculture practice to their sustained production.

Excepting oysters, periwinkles were the first and most enduring Irish shellfish export. Therefore they appear in the official statistics long before mussels do. In fact mussels were largely used for bait, not for human food, until the late nineteenth century and scallops did not enter trade until much later again. Clams and other species are only now beginning to appear in the statistics as commodities in their own right and not simply as contributors to the catch-all "miscellaneous" category. What all this signifies is the way in which the shellfish industry is growing, changing and developing. The traditional harvesters – the fishermen of the local coastal communities – have brought shellfish into a new era of cultivation, promotion and active management. In this they were enthusiastically supported, as we shall see in a later chapter, by developmental agencies such as BIM, the Marine Institute and Údarás na Gaeltachta, the developmental agency for the Irish-speaking regions.

The catalyst for the rapid modern development was the entry of Ireland into the EU – then the Common Market – in 1972. That event was also to trigger the explosive exploitation of the wild shellfish stocks that occurred in the ensuing decade. Today, the Irish shellfish industry generates over 28 million euro in export revenue and employs over 1,000 persons in the economy. Seafood is more easily obtained, more widely available, more extensively exported and more creatively presented now than ever before. The sheer exuberance of the various seafood festivals being held annually throughout Ireland proves that, at last, this ancient and valuable resource, deeply embedded in the folk culture, no longer constitutes *bia bocht* but is a valuable contributor to the commerce and cuisine of modern Ireland.

Chapter 2
LIMPETS, WINKLES AND WHELKS

A sweet, healthy food beside the hearth
on a cold spring afternoon when one is hungry.

Séamas Mac an Iomaire. Cladaigh Chonamara, *1938.*

It is a strange thing how, in some cultures, food is given the same status as those who eat it – champagne and caviar enjoy the same high esteem as those persons fortunate enough to partake frequently of them; beans and greens are not as highly prized, any more than those who, perforce, must live on them.

This hierarchy of respect is acknowledged in the old Irish saying regarding shellfish:

Bia Rí ruachan,
Bia bodach báirneach.
Bia caillighe faochóg,
A's á phiocadh le n-a snáthaid!

Which may be loosely rendered as:

For the King the cockle
And the limpet for the lout.
For the hag the winkle
With her pin to pick it out!
(Trans. NPW.)

One might well argue that the scallop or the oyster, rather than the cockle, is the real food of Kings. But few would deny that the humble limpet and winkle have been the predominant seafood of the ordinary people for thousands of years. They are, for example, the commonest items in many ancient shell middens and there are many Irish persons alive today who can remember eating them gratefully in less prosperous times. At the best of times limpets were a tough dish.

First they were boiled and then pan-roasted in a little fat. Around Galway Bay they were eaten widely earlier in the last century and people used to collect supplies to last for a few weeks. An oysterman in Galway Bay once told me that "eisters [oysters] were for selling and limpets for eating", a sentiment confirmed by a farmer friend raised in south Connemara. Together with winkles, whelks and the ormers – the latter a new, introduced species now cultivated in Ireland – they are members of the gastropod class of molluscs. Like their bivalve cousins, most gastropods are extremely fastidious herbivores and they select very carefully the algae they will eat. Their preferred food species are the micro-algae that attach to rocks and large seaweeds.

Three kinds of limpets (*Patella* species) were eaten in Ireland, the common kind called *An báirneach coitianta* and two others called *"broidirí"* and *"fianaigh"*. The latter two were said to be the best for eating. The large common limpet (*Patella vulgata*), also called *"an glas-báirneach"*, while not so good to eat, was regarded as good fishing bait for wrasse and sea bream. After gathering, boiling water was poured over them to free them from their shells. The flesh was then chewed before being worked onto the hook. That way the bait was softened and it was said to fish much better. Anyone who prepared bait regularly must surely have come to know only too well the different tastes, textures and qualities of the various kinds of limpet. The scalding, sucking, spitting and kneading of a baiting session can be imagined, as can the thirst it was likely to engender!

All limpets live firmly attached to rocks and stones and can be very difficult to remove unless one takes them by surprise, as it were. Rounded stones identified as "limpet hammers" supposedly used to detach limpets from their rocky grip, have been found by archaeologists at some very early coastal settlement sites. One would have thought that any old stone would have sufficed for the task of dislodging limpets and most stones on the beach are rounded by erosion. So, realistically, we must regard "limpet hammers" as a very tentative and speculative designation. But truth to tell, anyone who has tried to dislodge limpets without stealth or brute force will know just how difficult it is. They must, of course, let go their grip now and again in order to move around feeding on the tiny microscopic algae (Fig. 7). They feed normally when covered by the tide but when a heavy dew falls, or it rains, they are said to loosen their grip, get up and commence to wander about.

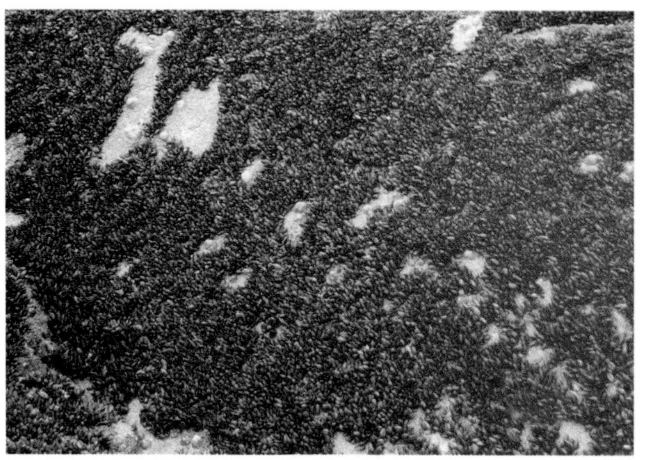

Fig. 7. The common limpet grazes a patch of rock keeping it free of settling mussels. This explains the bare patches seen in the carpet of mussels overlying the rocks on a Connemara shore. After feeding, the limpet returns to its original "home" spot on the rock and waits for the next tide before going "walkabout" again.

They were gathered in all seasons but most commonly in the spring and autumn. In Donegal, limpets were not considered to be good for eating until well after St. Patrick's Day and in other parts of the country it was said they were not at their best until they had experienced four high tides in April. Some limpets live high on the shore and in the spring of the year they would be covered for longer periods by the very high tides that occur then, so maybe there is some truth in the old tradition of when they are best for eating. It seems they were liked in some places more than others. In the Beara peninsula of Cork, *Bagún na farraige* (sea bacon) was the name given to them but whether that was because they were salty, or tasty, or just plain ordinary is not clear.

Collecting limpets on the rocky shore and out on the islands was not entirely without its risks and hazards. It was not unknown for people to be drowned by accident while out collecting, especially if marooned on isolated rocks when the boat that landed them failed to return before the tide did. One story from Dún Chaoin tells of a different, rather peculiar incident that befell a young woman there. She was out one day collecting limpets at Tráth an Dúinín in the parish of Múireach when she saw an apparition of the devil – *scáth an fhir thíos* – in the water beside her. This caused her to fall in. Nine months later she was delivered of a male child. When she took him to be baptised the priest enquired of her who the father was? She could not, or would not, tell him stating simply what she said had happened at the shore. So the priest named the child *Dúinín a' Mhúiraigh* after the place where he was apparently conceived. I suppose he felt it would be inappropriate to name such a child after a saint when his origin was so strange?

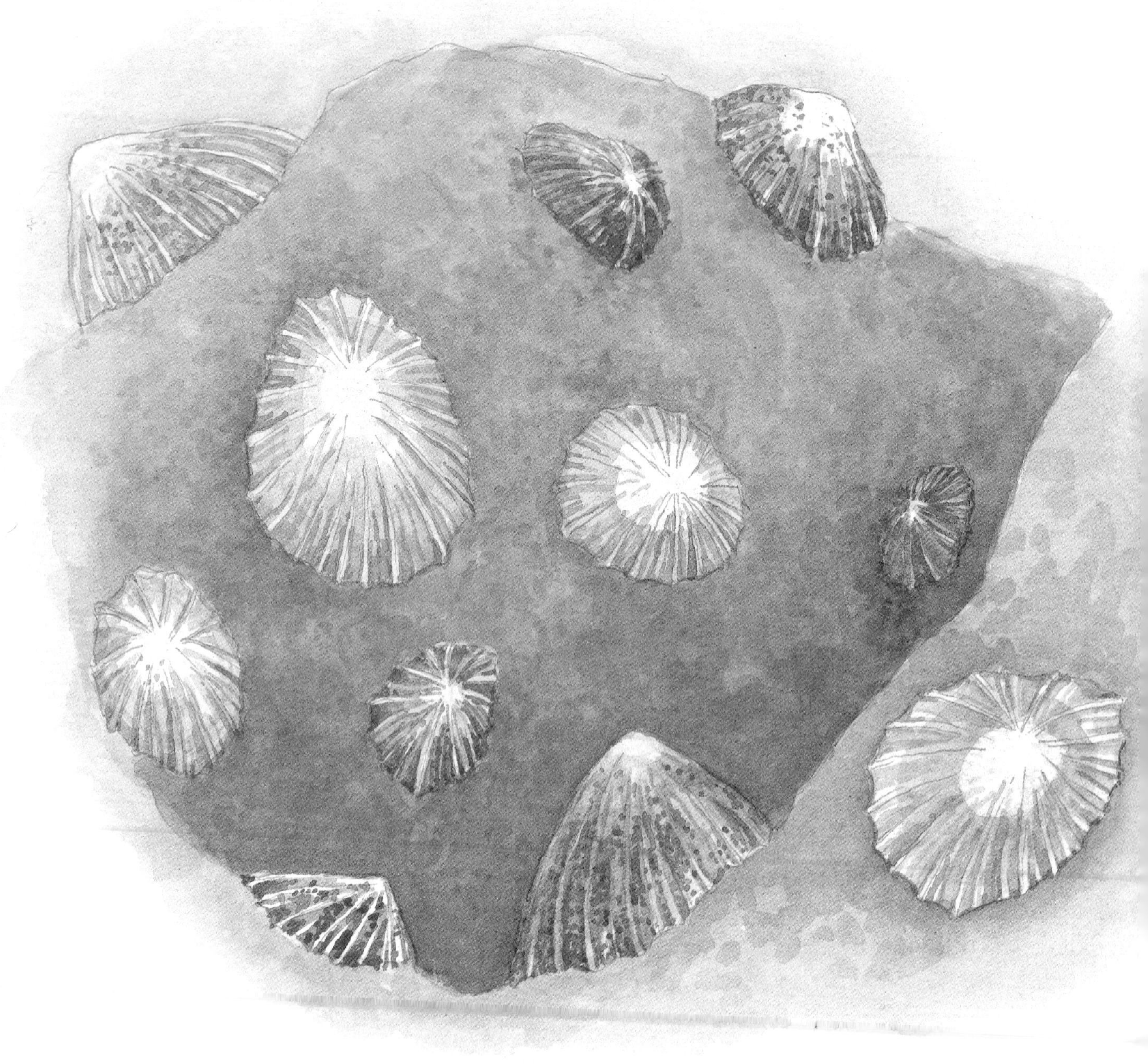

The child grew to be a handsome young man but at twenty-one years of age he left the house and was never seen again. Many an unchaperoned young woman must have met her young man out on a lonely shore on a fine spring day like this and nature must surely have taken its joyous course on some such occasions. After all, temptation is as easy to fall into as the sea and it is not for nothing that shellfish have a reputation as aphrodisiacs!

The spring tides around Easter were one of the great traditional collecting times for limpets and winkles in the west and south. *Rabharta mór an Earraigh*, sometimes called *Rabharta mór Phádraig*, was the name given to the exceptionally high and low tides experienced in that season and the "big strand" – the huge extent of foreshore that was exposed at low tide – made collecting easy and profitable. The period coincided roughly with the end of Lent when meat was not eaten and the weather around the equinox was often too severe to permit sea fishing in small boats and currachs. Stored food would also be low after the winter and before the new growing season got underway. For all these reasons, shellfish gathering was a common springtime chore and it was especially associated with Good Friday. There was, perhaps, little else to do on that penitential day when all the taverns were closed – and even empty too! Many persons still remember the tradition and some even regret it's passing into history within our own time.

In the north of the country it was customary to collect winkles even earlier in the year – around February 1st, *Lá fhéile Bhríde* (St. Brigid's Day) – and to place one in each corner of the house, so that no one could say that the house was without fresh food even in the leanest season. A variant of this story is told in the Beara peninsula. Here, the man of the house would go and bring back four limpets. He would throw one up into the roof space in each corner, saying "*Iasc beo Lá le Pádraig*" ("live fish on St. Patrick's Day!"). It was believed that if live fish were brought into a house on St. Patrick's Day (March 17th) that house would have an abundance of fish – *rath éisc* – for the whole year. Obviously some people did this on days other than St. Patrick's Day in order to appease, or maybe confuse, the Deity. In any case, a house from which a man would go fishing so early in the season (around the time of the equinoctial gales) was one where there was no great fear of the weather or the tides, so it is very unlikely that such an abode would lack for fish as the year progressed. But maybe that explanation makes too light of an ancient tradition? It is one unknown, or forgotten, in

Galway Bay even by those life-long winkle pickers who can still recall related customs. For example, one picker reared on Tawin Island in the inner Bay recalls how the man of the house went outside on New Year's Day and then re-entered the house exclaiming *"Beannacht Dé ar an dteach seo"* ("God bless this house!") as he entered – a form of the "first footing" tradition that is still practiced in Scotland. Irish was the language of Tawin early in the last century and it is still used to this day in naming places and things around the Bay. For example, the Tawin picker mentioned above and many others never refer to winkles as anything but "fweecauns" (= the Irish word *faochán*)

Limpets, winkles and to some extent mussels were used along with such seaweeds as carrageen (*Chondrus crispus*), sloke (*Porphyra* sp.) and dillisk (*Palmaria palmata*) to constitute what was termed "kitchen". Kitchen added piquancy to the rather boringly bland staple of potatoes that was the daily food of poor people. Kitchen was sometimes eaten between meals to assuage hunger but more often it was boiled in water or milk to accompany the spuds – rather like the Japanese use of delicacies in shoyu sauce as a condiment to accompany and enhance the staple rice of that country. Still today, the best Japanese meals comprise tasty morsels in salty shoyu accompanied by bowls of rice. Those familiar with such cuisine can testify to its surprisingly good taste and delicacy. Italians, too, make splendid meals from pasta and pesto, so the traditional "potatoes and kitchen" diet of the Irish coast was in essence little different from its equivalent in other cultures. Kitchen also had many medicinal uses, both for sick children and young animals and no doubt it provided valuable salts in a monotonous diet. Real men, naturally, got their medicine elsewhere which may have occasioned the traditional advice to drunkards ". . . avoid the drinking house or the limpet will be your food". Nowadays, limpets are not eaten at all in Ireland and there are almost no recipes, nor restaurants in which to sample them. Only once ever have I seen limpets on a menu and that was in the Canary Islands where they appeared as *Lapas con mojo*. They were not the same species as ours so maybe that dish does not count.

If you are adventuresome enough to try them, limpets can be tenderised with a meat mallet and then fried in butter with some chopped onions and garlic. Dip in shoyu sauce and eat. Otherwise, they can be cooked in traditional *Báirneach* soup, with or without some periwinkles, as described in the accompanying box.

Traditional Báirneach Soup

INGREDIENTS

1 large potato, peeled and chopped; 1 onion, chopped; 1 clove garlic (optional); 5 cups of limpets (or 4 of limpets and 1 of periwinkles); 2 pints fish stock or water; small bunch of dulse (the form called *creathnach* is best); small cup of cream; finely chopped parsley..

METHOD

Wash the shells well. Cook the potato and onion gently in butter for a few minutes. Add the shellfish, water and dulse and bring to the boil. Simmer until cooked. Strain off the soup and put aside. Remove shells and discard (remove and discard the operculum also if using periwinkles). Add the shellfish back into the soup. Thicken as required. Reheat and stir in the cream. Sprinkle with chopped parsley and serve with brown bread.

There are three common species of winkle only one of which – the common winkle *Littorina littorea,* called in Irish *an Fhaochóg* (or simply *an fhaocha* or *an fhaochán*) also *an gioradán,* is used for food. But unknown to many it has long been one of Ireland's star shellfish exports averaging almost 3,000 tonnes annually in recent years, valued at 2 million euro. Winkles are common in the intertidal part of most shores and they are easily picked off rocks and weeds. They do not cling on tightly like the limpet, but move about constantly on the stones and seaweed. When disturbed or in danger of drying out they withdraw into their shell and close a horny door, called the operculum, for complete protection. They can live a long time cooped up like this but of course they spend most of their time open, moving about and feeding, when left to themselves.

The topshell *Trochus umbilicatus* is known in Irish as *Faochán Mhuire,* the Virgin Mary's winkle. It too is a species with a horny operculum. How these animals came to have an operculum is the subject of a legend told on Clare Island in Clew Bay. St. Patrick, it seems, was chased all over Ireland by a band of enemies who eventually succeeded in catching and killing him, burying him deep in the ground. They then prepared their supper, boiling a cock in the pot. While waiting for it to cook, one of them asked whether there was any danger of the saint rising up again? The others calmed him with a laugh saying there was as much chance of Patrick rising up as there was of the cock in the pot rising up and crowing twelve times. The words were hardly spoken when the cock rose up and crowed loudly twelve times. The band realised that the saint had worked a miracle and was alive and free. So they took up the hunt again. Enquiring of a *ciaróg* (a black beetle, *Calathus cysteoides*) whether he had seen the Saint the beetle replied that he had. He was sheltering, the *ciaróg* said, in a *faochán* and not only that but he had miraculously put a cap (the operculum) on the shell so that he could be well covered when the snail drew itself in. Off went the band looking for the snail with the cap. Patrick naturally was one step ahead of them and had, in fact, put a cap on all the topshells and winkles on the shore. So the enemy could not find him among all the shells with an operculum, which served them right. Where would we be today if they had succeeded in killing our national patron saint before his work was done?

For their part, the *faochaí* were lucky it was St. Patrick and not St. Columcille they encountered. Of Columcille the story is told that he once met with a shoal of flounders migrating in the sea. "Is this a removal (a funeral)?" he enquired, civilly enough. "Yes it is, crooked legs" replied one of the flounders cheekily. The saint was piqued at this insolence and riposted "If I have crooked legs, may you have a crooked mouth". And so, to this day, the flounder's mouth is crooked and all to one side. Columcille went on to make his home on the Scottish island of Iona. The prevalence of the surnames Cameron (*cam srón,* meaning "crooked nose") and Campbell (*cam béal,* meaning "crooked mouth") in Scotland suggests that Columcille may have not have been entirely welcome or may have had an unreported dark side to his otherwise saintly nature!

Gathering winkles was women's and children's work mainly, requiring nothing but a bucket (a *galún*) or a small basket (a *ciseán* or a *cleibhín),* infinite patience and a willingness to work stooped-over for long periods (Fig. 8). Even though the gathering was done alone, the group outing to the shore and the return together were occasions for neighbourly chat. Anyone could collect winkles, but members of households living within walking distance of the shore were the main participants. In this way, unofficial "ownership" of different tracts of shore was established in some areas and these were recognised and respected by the community. In some instances the landlords charged extra rent for these tracts, maintaining an odious custom that goes back to the seventh century and that is mentioned in early records.

Fig. 8. Gathering winkles calls for a willingness to work stooped over for long periods – not at all an easy job. Note the galûn *(the small bucket), and the red mesh "onion bag" in the background. When the* galún *is full its contents are emptied into the bag.*

Fig. 9. Winkling can be hard on the hands too. Today, winkle gatherers often wear rubber gloves and waders or wellies, here worn under trousers by one of the gatherers in Galway Bay.

Winkles are traditionally said to make musical sounds as the tide ebbs. Modern collectors confirm that they make "bubbling and squeaking" sounds, both on the shore and when stored in bags. This is probably the sound of air escaping from underneath the shell as the temperature rises. They appear to like warmth – during the winter they congregate under stones and weed but in spring they come to the surface. On sunny days they are found on top of the stones and weed sunning themselves. This causes the shell to dry out making the animal more easily seen by the collector. When wet, the black shell merges more into the dark background.

The winkle-pickers followed the tide out and then preceded it in again, collecting all the time. Long ago they worked in their ordinary clothes and boots; today they dress in oilskins if the weather calls for these and wear "wellies" or waders instead of boots. Wearing waders it is possible to kneel down to the task, otherwise it is the usual stooped-over stance that is used and that really tells on the back. Plastic or rubber work gloves are normal nowadays too, as cuts to the hands sustained while picking are painful in the salty conditions (Fig. 9). It can be cold work, dangerous too, on the slippery rocks, and not everyone is willing to do it. Yet, the financial reward is not to be disdained. Many a child on the South Galway shore contributed to the cost of a first bicycle (and learned an important lesson in economics) by helping with the winkles. I am told they are not so willing to help nowadays and bicycles are no longer a big deal to them!

Gathering is concentrated around the period of low spring tides as the biggest winkles occur low on the shore. During neap tides winkles are sometimes collected in shallow, weedy lagoons. Around Tawin in South Galway the neap tide collection is called "mallure"collecting (from the Irish word "*mallmhuir*" meaning "neap tide"). "Mallure" winkles are not as highly regarded, either by collectors or dealers, as open shore winkles since they do not appear to be as hardy or as heavy as they might be. This is to be expected: because they live relatively higher up on the lagoon shore they are exposed for longer periods and therefore spend less time feeding so that their meat weight is usually very reduced.

When the bucket is full the periwinkles are turned into mesh onion bags that hold 25 kilograms. The bucket may hold around three kilos and about seven or eight buckets will fill a bag. At a good site the bucket can be filled in about twenty minutes. On a bad day it can take an hour to fill and that is really disappointing and frustrating for the collector. October to April is the best collecting period as the markets in France are eager for them and the prices are good. The shortage of collectors in the darkest winter months means that supplies can be low and prices consequently high at that time. After Christmas the market holds up until early summer although the price drops significantly as the season advances. Bags are stored on the lower shore or on a nearby pier. Bags stored on the pier long ago were doused with sea-water every now and again to keep the animals alive before they were collected, maybe weeks later, by a travelling dealer and taken on for sale elsewhere. Today, dealers collect the bags without delay and the winkles can appear on the foreign markets within days of collection.

Fig. 10. Storage ponds at Rock Island near Crookhaven, Co. Cork. These ponds were once used to store live lobsters, winkles, oysters and other seafood prior to export to France. They are now largely derelict.

Fig. 11. Present day view of the site of the Ardfry Experimental Oyster Station, Co. Galway, Ireland's first shellfish laboratory. Ernest Holt, a famous fishery biologist, established it in 1903 and it remained in operation until 1914. The low hill in the centre background is the site of the new Irish Marine Institute expected to be completed in 2005.

In the past, when there was a big strand, the winkle-pickers sometimes came upon oysters or the occasional scallop. These were real prizes that were secreted in separate bags lest the authorities or the Guards should happen along. When the coast was clear these windfall spoils were gathered up and taken away quietly.

Winkles are not farmed commercially although it is not uncommon to store them in large ponds while getting a decent shipment together. Ponds of this kind, dating from the early part of the twentieth century can still be seen near Crookhaven in Co. Cork (Fig. 10). Commercially valuable as winkles are, it is difficult to see how anyone could ever hope turn a good profit from breeding them artificially. That did not stop Ernest Holt, the Chief Inspector of Irish Fisheries, from proposing such a course at the Ardfry Experimental Oyster Cultivation Station, Ireland's first shellfish laboratory, in 1905 (Fig. 11). In what must have been a rush of blood to the head, he instructed his young assistant Walter Tattersall to "... start a winkle farm!" telling him how to set about it. This involved planting timber stakes in the sea on which winkles were supposed to climb and be counted and measured regularly. It was not really a farm, but it was what Holt specified. Later on Holt instructed "... It is also most desirable that we should know when and how winkles breed ... If you could work it out it would be of some importance scientifically as well as for economic purposes".

Fig. 12. Walter Tattersall, who set up a "winkle farm" at Ardfry on the instructions of Ernest Holt. Tattersall left Ardfry to become curator of Manchester Museum in 1909. Eventually he served at the front in World War 1. Later he became Professor of Zoology in the University of Wales at Cardiff. Photo courtesy of Crustaceana.

Tattersall, born in Bootle, Lancashire in 1882, had joined Holt's staff in 1902 after graduating from Liverpool University (Fig. 12). He proved to be a talented and dedicated scientist who carried out Holt's instructions to the letter. So he commenced an attempt to breed periwinkles in glass dishes under very poor experimental conditions – his "laboratory" was a converted deckhouse, taken from an old brigantine that had previously served as a floating marine laboratory. The deckhouse had been transferred to land at the Oyster Station at Ardfry and it constituted the Station's main building as well as the sleeping quarters for the watchman at night! As we can imagine, much of the work necessarily demanded simple, cheap but effective solutions to the problems at hand and Tattersall's description of his winkle breeding equipment and technique gives us a flavour of how things were done:

> " . . . Considerable difficulty was at first experienced in rearing them through the various stages of their development. I was at first compelled to adopt the crude method of keeping the eggs in shallow dishes and changing the sea water frequently. This method was not successful, since it encouraged the rapid multiplication of numerous species of Infusoria which attacked the eggs . . . Finally I hit on a simple method which proved successful. A large glass jam jar was filled with fresh sea water which had been strained through the finest bolting silk. The eggs were transferred to the jar, and the mouth of the jar was covered by a piece of the same bolting silk tied on with string or thread. The jar was then submerged in the sea. By this means the temperature of the water in the jar was kept the same as the surrounding sea, and all extraneous matter likely to harbour infusoria was excluded by the silk covering of the jar mouth. Under these conditions development proceeded smoothly".

With this simple, empirical approach Tattersall was able to observe and describe, for the very first time, the life cycle of the common periwinkle. He also continued with his observations on winkles climbing the stakes as instructed by Holt and sought out evidence of natural spawning of periwinkles on the shore. He hoped to continue his observations in greater detail even after he left Ardfry, but as he wrote many years later, ". . . Circumstances have prevented me from accomplishing this work . . . ". He did not indicate that the "circumstances" involved active service at the front in Flanders during the Great War where, in Holt's words, ". . . [He] is supplying the mathematics of a heavy gun battery, entirely contented with the job". He was later wounded and gassed in that awful conflict. He wrote up his periwinkle observations in 1920, referring to the timber stakes as "the winkle farm", always using inverted commas. He obviously realized that they did not constitute a farm in any real sense of the word, but that was the term that Holt had used and Tattersall was loyal to his old mentor. He went on to become Professor of Zoology in Cardiff, Wales and maintained his Irish connections through regular field trips to Lough Ine in County Cork. He died in 1943. Holt had died in 1922. Both men are illustrious in the pantheon of eminent marine biologists. The new laboratory and headquarters of the Irish Marine Institute are in course of erection at a site in Galway Bay overlooking the old Ardfry Experimental Oyster Station. It is devoutly to be hoped that the names of these two great pioneers will be suitably acknowledged within that wonderful new marine science facility.

For eating, winkles are steamed or boiled and then picked out of the shell with a pin or needle. This is too much hassle for many modern people who deem them hardly worth the effort. So, when we look at the statistics for the export of periwinkles – over 2,600 tonnes in 1998 – we can only wonder who eats so many of them? And these are only the Irish export statistics. Over 2,000 tonnes are gathered in Scotland each year also and perhaps the same amount in other parts of the United Kingdom. Since the vast majority is exported to continental markets the answer to the question comes easily – the French, Spanish and Dutch are the great consumers of winkles.

One can still buy winkles in Ireland today, already cooked, at some sea-side resorts, along with dillisk and carrageen moss – two kinds of seaweed much used and prized in Ireland long ago. No summer visit to Lahinch (spelt Lehinch on road signs, a seeming gender change of unknown significance) or to other West Clare resorts is complete without partaking of them. They are sold in paper bags of about 200 grams costing two euro (Fig. 13). In Omeath at Carlingford Lough there were as many as eight sellers' stalls at one time but nowadays there is only one. Winkles are, in fact, quite tasty when simply boiled in salt water. Traditionally in Ireland they were used along with limpets to make soup eaten as a cure for a cold. Used as kitchen they were boiled, removed from their shells and then added to the salt water in which the potatoes were cooking.

Fig. 13. "What are winkles, Daddy?" A young father introduces his daughter, up on her toes to see the bags, to the pleasure of winkles at Lahinch Co. Clare.

That way they flavoured the potatoes. Presented more elaborately, like Escargot de Bourgogne, winkles can hold their own in the most august Gallic company. One can imagine they would go well in chowder and in paella and risotto too.

Nowadays, all winkles are graded prior to export. Even here, Tattersall had something mathematical to say. He realised that the dealer estimated the average size of winkles in a bag to be closer to the smallest than to the largest individuals he could see and therefore he (the dealer) paid less for the whole bag. Tattersall suggested that by grading three bags of mixed winkles into one bag of large size individuals and two bags of the smaller ones, the dealer could be induced to pay more, on aggregate, than he would for three ungraded bags. Still today, the larger grade of winkle pays more than the smaller and some– the smallest ones usually – are used not as food for humans, but as live grazers of seaweed and so fetch a very poor price. Placed into the mesh bags in which bivalves such as oysters and scallops are cultivated, the small winkles graze the settling algae and in that way keep the bags clean so that water can flow freely into and through them. In due course the winkles grow larger and can then be sold for human consumption.

There are a number of gastropods that are not algal grazers. Some in fact are among the most voracious predators and scavengers in the sea. The best known are the dog whelk, *Nucella lapillus* and the common whelk, or buckie, *Buccinum undatum*. The dog whelk, *an fhaocha chapaill* or *an pachrán* in Irish, is common on sheltered shores. It feeds by boring a hole in the shell of its victim – usually a bivalve mollusc – and then sucking out its flesh. From the Bronze Age, perhaps even from the late Mesolithic period, until the early Christian period dog whelks were gathered by coastal communities of the west of Ireland, not for use as food but for the purple dye that can be extracted from them. Shells gathered for this purpose were broken in a characteristic way that makes it easy to distinguish them in shell middens. They are particularly common in middens in Galway and Mayo.

The common whelk or buckie, which is a denizen of deeper water, was called the "sugarloon" in olden times and its Irish name is *an chuachma*. Oysters, mussels, scallops and any other shellfish sessile enough to find themselves in the way of the buckie are fair game to it. Using its rasping radula like the dog whelk, it bores through its victim's shell and then sucks out the flesh of the poor unfortunate. The empty shell of the buckie is found on many sandy shores and children will know it as the Irish shell most commonly put to their ear to "hear the sea" which, as we know, is just the amplified sound of their own blood coursing through their veins. The whelk was never eaten in Ireland to any great extent although in Achill and other places it was eaten on occasions. Its main value was as a bait species. Because they live in deeper water whelks are not easy to gather commercially unless one has a reasonably substantial boat from which to lay down a line of pots or creels. Historically, most of the Irish shellfish gatherers were tenant farmers rather than full time fishermen and most had only small and inadequate rowboats, if they had any boat at all. They rowed out a little and captured the whelks in wicker pots baited with decaying fish or offal. They were then stored in bags or boxes on the shore to be used as bait for long lines when necessary. Whelks also entered lobster pots and crab creels, attracted by the bait and for their pains were made into fish bait themselves by the fishermen. The better class of fishes like cod, haddock, hake and ling were traditionally taken on baited long lines, so the whelk played an important role in these fisheries.

Fig. 14. Boxes of whelks freshly landed at Arklow await collection by the processor who will prepare them for export to Asian customers. In the background is a boat once used in the whitefish fleet but now fishing whelks.

They are most abundant on the east coast, but just like the oyster and mussel beds close to the shore became exhausted the whelk stocks also declined and the stocks that remained were those located in deeper water. By 1960 there was only a small trade in Irish whelks. Seeking out new products in 1980, Lett and Co. of Wexford encouraged a handful of fishermen from Arklow to fish further offshore where once again they came upon the whelk stock. To this day the centre of the modern whelk fishery is still off Wicklow with about 40 boats landing 40 to 50 boxes each per day from the beds located up to 25 kilometres offshore (Fig, 14). Each boat works 500 to 600 pots (often homemade from plastic containers, Fig. 15) setting them early in the morning and raising them in the early afternoon.

Fishery regulations require that whelks below 5 centimetres in length and 2.5 centimetres in width be returned to the sea as a means of ensuring conservation of the stocks. Crabmeat and dogfish are the baits used to lure the scavenging whelks into the pots (Fig. 16). Other edible species taken in baited pots include crabs and lobsters, which are Crustaceans, not Molluscs. This has lead one company to develop special baits that attract one particular species while repelling another, a most clever way to "target" the desired species for capture. One species' meat is another's poison and it shows again that being "picky" about food is all very well but it can be turned against one!

The Irish whelk fishery has almost doubled between 1997 and 2001 when the catch was over 6,000 tonnes with an export value in excess of 8 million euro – not bad for an erstwhile much-despised species! Some boats and crews have left the whitefish fleet and have turned to seeking out new whelk stocks in other parts of Ireland especially off the north and south coasts. All catches are processed in Ireland and then exported, so they make a double contribution to local employment and to the national economy. Whelks are a firm favourite in Asia, which is the main destination of Irish exports, placing them among the best-travelled Irish shellfish these days. However, there is still no consumer market for them in Ireland.

Fig. 15. Plastic containers being readied as whelk pots. A large hole is cut in the side of the containers to make the entrance or the mouth. Smaller holes are drilled in all surfaces to allow water to enter and leave the pot as it is being shot and hauled. A stone or piece of concrete is placed inside to weigh the pot down. Individual pots will be linked together with ropes passed through the handles.

Fig. 16. A cylindrical piece of netting is attached to the mouth of the pot to make the "throat" that prevents the whelks from climbing out. The bait – crabmeat or dogfish flesh is usual – is attached inside the pot.

The Real Molly Malone?

The idea that Molly Malone was a real person who lived in the seventeenth century has been described as "a bizarre legend of glorious implausibility" by John Murphy, author of *The Mystery of Molly Malone.*

The song *Alive, Alive-O* was not known before 1850 and the version sung today does not predate the 1880s. The earliest known published versions appeared in 1883 and 1884. It is probably the work of James Yorkston, a Scot, and it may be that a real fisher girl living in Dublin was the inspiration for the words of the song. For many, the true image of Molly Malone is one of an imaginary young fishmonger in late Victorian Dublin.

From 1883 to 1891, James Pearse and Edmund Sharp carried on business as sculptors at 27 Great Brunswick Street (now named Pearse Street), Dublin. James the principal partner, who lived on the premises, was the father of Pádraig Pearse the teacher, revolutionary and 1916 leader who was born at this address in 1879. Pádraig's brother William, born here in 1881, followed in his father's footsteps as a sculptor before going to Paris to study art. He co-founded Scoil Enda with his brother and taught art there. He too was to die by execution as a consequence of the 1916 rising.

The picture here shows a small Victorian bust entitled "Fisher girl", inscribed on the back "P and S Dublin" by its manufacturers. Surely this is the work of the Pearse and Sharp business? If so, it is a contemporaneous representation of a typical Dublin fisher girl of the period when the famous "Alive, Alive-O" was written. As such, does this have a better claim to represent the "real Molly Malone" than other, more modern, representations? Its connection with the Pearse brothers, who were school children at the time of its manufacture at their home, makes it especially appropriate as a true Dublin icon.

MUSSELS

Crying cockles and mussels, alive alive-o!

Popular folk song.

THE COMMON OR BLUE MUSSEL, *Mytilus edulis*, (*an diúilicín* in Irish) is the most abundant, most widespread and most versatile of the Irish shellfish. There is hardly a solid rock, stone, pier, rope or other structure in the sea that does not carry its burthen of mussels; likewise, there is hardly a seafood dish that cannot be enhanced by a helping of them.

The young of the mussel spends its earliest weeks free-swimming in the water before settling on any suitably hard or fibrous surface, like timber, rocks and ropes. This first settlement is followed a few weeks later by a second migration when they take to the water column again and are carried along to another locale. Their second settlement is their final one, and very often they choose to settle under and among older, larger mussels. There they secrete strong attachment fibres, called the byssus or beard, to hold them secure. The expansion of the new young mussels as they grow bigger crowds out the older ones overlying them, which eventually become detached and fall to the bottom. If conditions are good the young will grow to maturity in about two years and the lifecycle will start over again.

Often they settle in the intertidal zone where they are not immersed in water all the time and growth is consequently slower. As mussels get older, the shell tends to become thick and "stony" with a pronounced blue-black colour. When they grow suspended in the water column they are immersed all of the time and so they grow more quickly. The shell is then much less stony, more brittle and more of a brown or striped colour. Mussels that grow in the intertidal zone learn naturally to close their shells as the tide goes out and they become

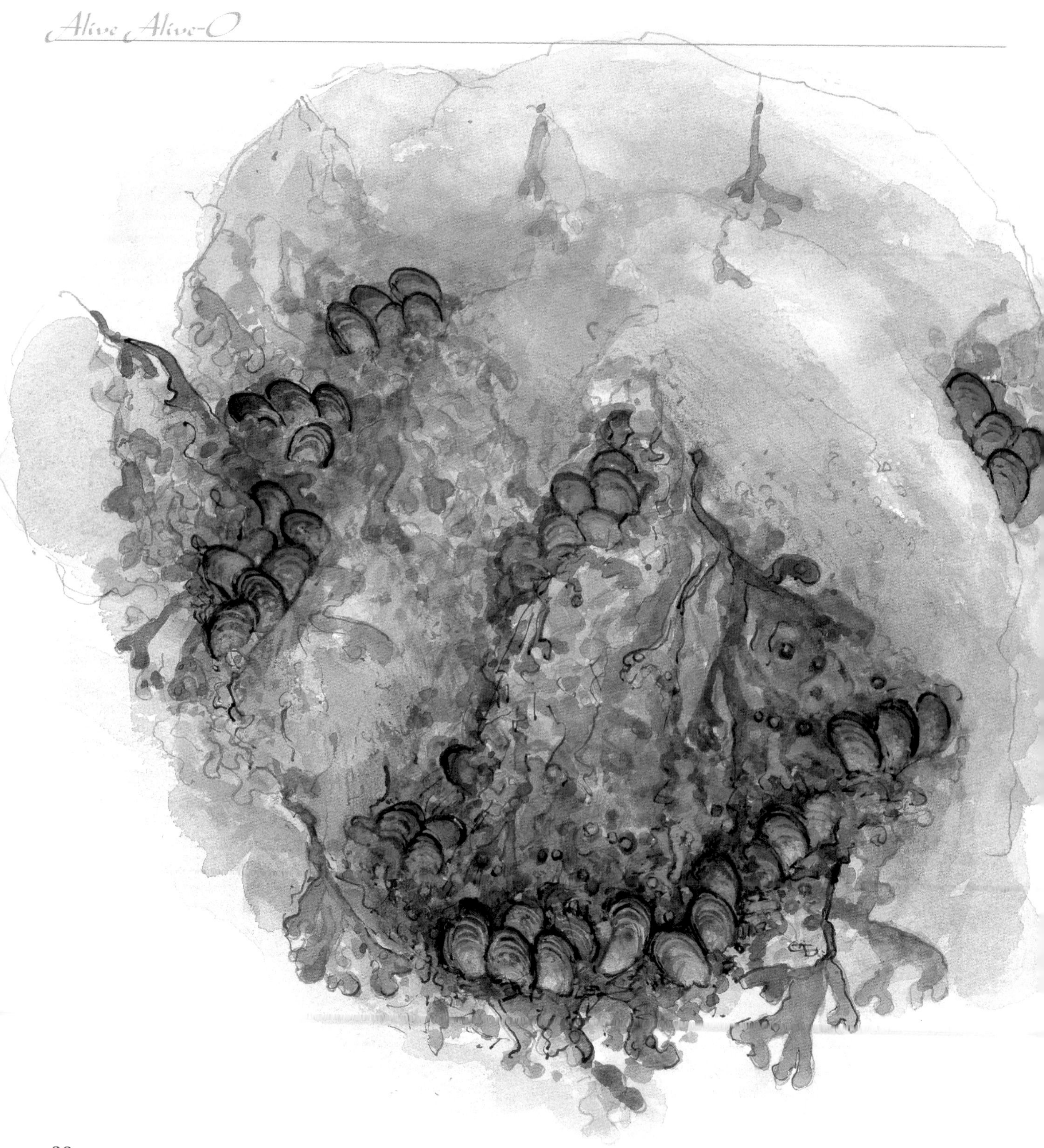

exposed to the air. But very strangely, those that grow permanently under water must be trained to close up when exposed out of the water. Leaving them in bags on the shore for two or three tidal cycles, where they soon learn the need to shut up, does this. It is important to train them in this way when they are harvested and before they are sent to market. If they did not close their shells they would not survive transportation out of water very long. So maybe the lesson of the mussel is to keep one's mouth shut if one wishes to go far!

The huge numbers of young and the security of their attachment to protective structures ensure that mussels occur in enormous abundance in suitable areas, that is on rocky coasts, moderately exposed as well as sheltered, and in river estuaries. Successful production requires both good growth and fattening of adults together with reliable recruitment of new juveniles every year. There is some suggestion that the particular mussel found on some exposed Irish shores is the Mediterranean mussel, (*Mytilus galloprovincialis*), which differs somewhat from the blue mussel. The difference is important mainly to zoological experts who relish nothing as much as lively scientific debate. In Ireland the principal areas from which wild mussels were commercially harvested and exported were Wexford Harbour, Cork Harbour, Castlemaine Harbour, Galway Bay, Sligo Bay, the Foyle Estuary, Belfast Lough, Carlingford Lough and Dundalk Bay, especially the estuary of the River Boyne. In all these places the mussels grew naturally on the sea-bottom. Accessibility – both to the beds and to suitable means of transport – as much as abundance determined what were good mussel harvesting areas.

Most mussels were gathered, by hand picking or by dredging, in the period between autumn and late spring and were shipped to Liverpool and Manchester for human consumption. About 2,000 tons were exported annually at the start of the twentieth century. In Belfast, the working classes took large quantities at holiday times (there the mussel was often called "the poor man's oyster") but the main catch was normally sent to the fishing ports of the east coast of Scotland for use as bait in the long line fisheries. In Ireland too they were commonly used as bait, but around Galway in the 1830s they were "used in considerable quantities by the poorer classes, for food" according to one contemporary source. The same was true in other districts. In some parts of Donegal and Cork mussels were spread on the fields as fertilizer and were considered to be especially good as manure for potatoes. For local use, whether as bait, fertilizer or human food, most areas in Ireland had adequate stocks and those in the know could gather a good meal from the intertidal zone at low tide in a matter of minutes, at no cost and with almost no effort at all. This is still true today. Such small-scale local consumption made absolutely no impact on trade statistics, leading to the erroneous opinion that mussels were not eaten in Ireland at all. Tell that to Molly Malone!

The cultivation of mussels took off in the 1970s and nowadays mussels and salmon are two of Ireland's most successfully cultivated seafood species. But their association goes back much further – to the thirteenth century in fact – and mussel cultivation by the "French" *bouchot* method is an old Irish invention. The technique is one in which mussels are grown attached to timber poles set vertically in shallow, soft-bottomed bays that have a big tidal range. The story goes as follows:

In 1235 a boat trading between Ireland and France was shipwrecked on the French coast near La Rochelle. The captain, a man named Walton, was the only survivor along with some sheep. Thankful for his delivery, he settled on the shore of the Bay of Aiguillon where he is credited with crossing his surviving sheep to local stock and thereby originating a new race called marsh sheep, useful indeed in that *marais* region.

In those times, the commonest form of fish trap used in Ireland was the V-shaped fish weir used to catch salmon and other species on their shoreward migration. This consisted of two palisades made of stakes interwoven with branches, set in a V shape in an estuary with the apex of the V facing the sea. The apex was closed with a net bag. The flooding tide brought fish into the estuary, over the tops of the palisades. Later as the tide receded, the fish were corralled behind the palisades and gradually funnelled into the bag-net from which they could subsequently be removed when the tide was out. Walton set up such a trap in the Bay, with arms about 400 yards long, hoping to harvest what fish he could (Fig. 17). Noting that the structure attracted sea birds that skimmed along the surface of the retreating tide (possibly tracking the captured fish), he attached aerial nets to the poles of the trap. In this way he was able to ensnare birds while capturing fish, ensuring that he made a good living by his inventiveness. God, as we know, helps those who help themselves and He was particularly helpful to Walton. Not only did his trap capture fish and fowl plentifully but also the poles and branches were soon covered with mussel spat! Remember that young mussels (spat) have a propensity to settle on hard or fibrous surfaces and the only such surfaces in the muddy Aiguillon Bay were Walton's stakes and poles. His neighbours quickly realised the benefit to be derived from these new structures and further poles and stakes were erected in the Bay to capture and rear more and more mussels. Thus was born the "French" *bouchot* system of mussel cultivation still in use to this very day!

Fig. 17. Nineteenth century engraving of the palisades and the "pousse-pied" boat invented by Walton in the thirteenth century to harvest mussels in the Bay of Aiguillon, France. The modern technique of bouchot culture is said to have evolved from palisades like these.

Fig. 18. Eighteenth century engraving from Diderot's great Encyclopedie *of a fisherman wearing mud skis called "platins" in France and "scooches" in Wexford.*

Walton is credited with devising one other useful invention. The Bay of Aiguillon is a huge expanse of mud at low tide, so fluid that it is difficult to traverse on foot. To facilitate safe passage to men working the traps, he invented the *pousse-pied,* a kind of very small boat. It consisted of a flat plank called the sole to which low, light plank strakes and a stern were nailed. The boatman balanced on one knee on the sole board inside the boat, with the other leg draped over the side where it served both as an oar and a rudder by pushing into the mud (Fig. 17). In this way man and craft could glide easily over the mud. In Ireland we have no craft like this. An alternative mode of progression was to attach short, ski-like boards to both feet and ski over the mud. Such devices are illustrated in Diderot's great *Encyclopedie* (Fig. 18) and we had similar devices in

Ireland, even in our own day. They were common on the Wexford slobs where they were known as "scooches" and they performed the same function there as we see in old French fishing prints. In figure 19 we see the late Tony Whilde wearing a pair of short scooches called "mud shoes" in Galway Bay in the 1960s. There are examples of scooches in the local museum at Rosslare Harbour in Wexford. So maybe Walton was a Wexford man? But whatever he was, he was inventive and innovative and he may be considered the father of Irish shellfish culture. Attempts to grow mussels by the bouchot method in Ireland in the 1970s did not prove very successful and were overtaken rapidly by the development of suspended cultivation using rafts and long lines.

Fig. 19. The late Dr.Tony Whilde wears special short scooches over his boots in the Clarinbridge oyster fishery in the 1960s. Photo: Marianne Whilde.

The principal modern centres for the commercial harvesting of wild, naturally grown mussels are Castlemaine Harbour in Kerry, Dundalk Bay and, until the last five years, the mouth of the River Boyne in County Louth. At Castlemaine in particular the stocks are still self-sustaining so that no seed mussels need to be introduced from outside the area of production. Provided that the natural beds are not over-exploited, which is not always the case, stock can be profitably and sustainably gathered in most years. In Wexford, on the other hand, where the local stock was greatly reduced long ago, young seed mussels from elsewhere are laid on the beds each year to grow and fatten. We will deal with this kind of mussel culture in the next chapter.

Fig. 20. Two large mussel dredges. Traditional dredges were smaller when the dredgers were powered by sail or by rowing. Large, modern powered dredgers can tow much heavier gear like that here. Note the deep well in the boat into which the dredged mussels are deposited.

Normally, wild mussels are harvested with boats pulling one or more dredges. The common dredge consists of a triangular metal frame with teeth on its horizontal base and a net bag attached to it (Fig. 20). It is pulled along the bottom by a boat under sail or power, or in the olden times one rowed by a crew. Dredges were much smaller and lighter, for obvious reasons, when the boats were rowed or sailed. The teeth of the dredge scrape the bottom and the mussels and debris collected are gathered in the net bag. The old style dredges (Fig. 44) did not always stay on the bottom when being towed. Sometimes they "skipped" along, alternately dredging and overflying the bed. Every so often the dredge is raised and the contents of the bag are turned out. The mussels are retained and the debris thrown overboard. Since the mussels grow on the sea bottom in the natural way they tend to have slightly heavier, thicker shells with a higher meat yield and a darker flesh colour. Bottom grown mussels are particularly desirable in the Dutch market where they are preferred to the rope- and bouchot-cultured varieties, probably because the native Dutch beds were mostly beds of bottom-grown mussels.

Fig. 21. One compartment of the large mussel purification plant erected at Cromane Co. Kerry by the Sea Fisheries Association in 1940. It was filled with clean sea water in which the mussels were steeped for some days to clear them of any impurities prior to sale. The plant has not been used for a long time.

Cromane at Castlemaine in Co. Kerry is one of the best-known traditional mussel villages where up to forty families made a living from dredging. Each boat had two men who took up the mussel work when the salmon season ended. They rowed out to find a good patch of mussels, which they called a "pitch" (football metaphors pervade the minds of Kerrymen) and they dredged that until the boat was full. By then it was low in the water and rowing home could be quite hazardous. The catch was landed on the beach, graded through a riddle, cleaned and then packed in hundredweight sacks for export by rail from Killorglin to the English dealers. In 1940 the Sea Fisheries Association, the predecessor of BIM, built a purification plant to depurate the mussels prior to dispatch (Fig. 21). This improved the marketability of the product and harvesting increased from about two hundred to seven hundred tonnes through the 1950s. At that time the mussels were brought to the plant by donkey and cart from the landing place. Even today, because of the lack of any pier, mussels are loaded from the dredgers onto trailers that are reversed with tractors into the sea at low water and then taken to the packing stations.

Outboard engines were not introduced into the Cromane fishery (or indeed to many other Irish shellfisheries) until the 1960s. The first man to buy and use an engine experienced the problem, normal with early outboards, of frequent engine cutout, especially when it was damp or the stern was swamped by water. He was, nevertheless, so successful that others discouraged him from venturing out in inclement weather by calling to him as they passed his house ". . . It's no day for steam!" Inevitably the others came to buy engines of their own in due course but for quite a while these were used only for pulling the dredge; for going out to the pitch and coming back, the engine was shut down and the men rowed as usual. Old customs do not die easily! Even the donkey and cart (or creel) was in use as lately as the 1980s to bring mussels from the boats to the articulated trucks parked in Cromane that were to take them onwards to the French market.

Two processing plants were opened in Killorglin in 1958 and these gave much needed employment mainly to women for a few years, after which they closed and the fishery declined. A decade or so later a local fishery cooperative was formed and began to manage the beds under a Mussel Fishery Order and Fish Culture Licence. Under the new scheme bottom culture activities based on Dutch cultivation methods were commenced. These are similar to those operated in Wexford Harbour and will be described in the next chapter.

The mussels harvested from the estuary of the River Boyne are not, strictly speaking, dredged mussels. They are more "raked and scraped" mussels, collected by a technique now unique to that locality in Ireland and still in use there. It requires a special boat and a special long-handled mussel rake.

The mussel boat is quite different from the cobble used for salmon draft netting at the mouth of the Boyne. It is a heavy, but shallow-draft, clinker-built vessel, 18 feet long and 5 feet in the beam (Fig. 22). It is made from fifteen planks, comprising the keel plank, made of beech and seven white deal strakes on each side. Both the stem and the stern are squared off, but the stem is narrower. There is a large indentation in the stern through which the single oar is manipulated as a paddle. The flat stem is pierced with a hole through which the anchor rope is threaded (Fig 23). Internally, the ribs are made of larch. There are no rowlocks or thole-pins and only one thwart, positioned about one third of the distance from the stern. A large, removable platform is constructed in the forward part of the boat (from about the third to the seventh ribs) and it is on

Fig. 22. A mussel boat used for raking mussels at Mornington in the estuary of the River Boyne. Note the platform on which the fisherman stands and the indentation in the stern through which a single oar is used as a paddle.

Fig. 23. A River Boyne mussel boat. Note the shallow, clinker construction, the blunt stem pierced with a hole through which the forward anchor rope is threaded, the fishing platform, the single thwart towards the stern and the butyl rubber lining of the boat well. Note also the absence of rowlocks and thole-pins.

this that the fisherman stands when using the rake. Behind the platform the well of the boat is empty and can carry up to one tonne of mussels. Sometimes it is floored with sheet metal or butyl rubber so that it is easier to clean out when the work is done. When not in use the boats lie up on a small beach behind the site of the old fishmeal factory near the estuary mouth at Mornington.

The rake is not unlike a large, metal grass or hay rake but is much heavier and the handle, made of larch, is up to 20 feet long (Fig. 24). Strips of metal are welded to the rake head to form a slotted backing plate. The tines are made of steel and are set close together (Fig. 25).

Mussel raking usually takes place from October to March when there is no salmon fishing. There is one person to each boat. Three hours after high tide he sculls out into the river using a single broad-bladed oar. The ebb tide and the current of the river are running strongly together so he needs little extra propulsion to move rapidly downstream. When he arrives at his chosen spot (he generally starts where he last obtained a catch, or where one of his colleagues was successful, or where for any reason or from previous experience he judges that he will find mussels) he throws out the anchor from the bow and the boat continues to drift stern-first down the current until the anchor holds and the short anchor rope tautens. The boat is now fixed in the current, facing upstream. He then throws a second anchor – called the tail – over the stern. The tail can be a sack weighted with stones or a bucket pierced with holes. The latter acts as a sheet anchor, the former as a normal bottom anchor. Fore and aft anchors are absolutely essential if the boat is to be held steady facing into the flow without yawing as the fisherman works the rake along the bottom. The blunt stem is an extra help in keeping the boat steady facing into the current.

Standing on the platform, the fisherman throws the rake in an underhand throw as far forward (upstream) as possible, feeding the handle through his hands and using them to propel the rake out as far as possible. He grabs the end of the handle when the device has been propelled to its maximum distance. It may be thrown to the left or the right of the anchor rope, as each individual prefers. The heavy rake head sinks to the bottom and the experienced fisherman can tell from his grip on the handle whether the rake is lying on mussels or rock or mud. The force of the current helps the rake head to bite into the bottom

Fig. 24. The Boyne mussel rake is up to 20 feet long, making Leo Boyle seem small! Leo is a long-time fisherman of Mornington.

Fig. 25. The head of a Boyne mussel rake. The long tines are stainless steel; the back and sides are made of strips of metal welded to the iron frame of the rake.

sufficiently to snag the mussels. Too great a force will cause the bite to be too firm and the head to lodge deep into the substrate, leading to difficulties in drawing it back. If the force of the current is not strong enough the bite will be inadequate and the rake will not properly snag, or get good leverage on, the mussels. Similarly, if the water depth is too great, the rake head will not sink as fast as it should (a greater amount of buoyant handle will be in the water and will retard the sinking of the head) and the bite will be less.

The rake is now jutting out ahead of the boat and at an angle of about 45 degrees to the surface of the water. The fisherman pulls the rake towards himself, on the left or the right of the boat as the case may be, in small, jerky tugs, passing the handle over his outside shoulder as the rake head draws nearer (Fig. 26). The tines scrape the mussels and weed from the bottom, gathering them between the tines and the slotted back and side plates. When the rake has been drawn back until it is almost vertical and is now beside the boat, the fisherman gives a final sharp tug and commences to lift the rake backwards into the boat. When the rake lifts off the bottom, the force of the current can wash the mussels out of it. The fisherman therefore rotates the handle so that the tines of the rake face into the current and the mussels can be raised lying on the back plate of the rake head, kept in by the tines (Fig. 27). Leo Boyle, a local salmon netsman and long-time mussel fisherman who features in the accompanying pictures, described the process in the following brilliantly descriptive manner: The mussel rake is like one's hand with the fingers bent to resemble the tines and the downward facing palm resembling the back plate of the rake. Like that, one can scrape items very efficiently off a submerged surface using the bent fingers. But to lift the items up without closing the fist (especially if there is a strong current flowing through the bent fingers towards the wrist) one has to rotate the hand so that the items lie in the upturned palm, guarded by the bent fingers and then they can be safely lifted.

The mussels are dropped into the well of the boat and the process is repeated until sufficient numbers are collected. Two or three bags would normally suffice for a day's raking. Once a fisherman finds himself on a good "vein" of mussels – a cluster of, say, fifteen feet long and a few feet broad – he will work the vein systematically until he has cleared it all to his boat. The boat can be moved from place to place if necessary but it is more convenient if a good vein is encountered and worked thoroughly.

Fig. 26. The rake is pulled in, passing it over the left or right shoulder depending on which side of the boat is being worked.

Fig. 27. The rake is lifted into the boat with the tines facing upstream so that the current forces the mussels on to the back plate of the rake. The fisherman is now facing the stern of the boat.

As the tide ebbs the flow diminishes progressively so that close to low tide the flow is not sufficient for raking. With a low flow, the boat is not held firmly against the pull of the rake: instead of the rake coming towards the boat, the boat is pulled towards the sunken rake head and there is no leverage on the mussels. So the fisherman really has only about three hours of good fishing conditions – less in neap tides – before he must come in. Sometimes he will fish one hour of the flood tide, this time with the boat facing downstream into the flood, but mostly he hopes to be home before then. When he lands, the mussels are shovelled out onto the beach where they are cleaned of weed and debris and bagged for transport. Before the 1940s they could be sent directly to market; more recently, because of changes in the quality of the water, they are first sent to depuration facilities in Wexford or Bantry before being sold.

This traditional technique, depending as it does on the strength of the river current, the flow of the ebb tide and the depth of the water, all of which can vary from tide to tide and with differing conditions of wind and freshwater runoff, demands a very fine appreciation of flow conditions in the estuary at the time of fishing. Mussel raking is therefore a skill that cannot be mastered properly without considerable practical experience. For generations it provided a good living to families in Mornington who sent off bags of mussels weekly to the Manchester and Liverpool markets and who collected their "mussel cheques" from the post office in Drogheda with welcome regularity. They enjoyed prosperity from mussels at a time when other communities were not so fortunate, especially during the War years. The fishery has declined considerably in recent times and has not been carried out at all for four or five years. During that time the entrance to the port of Drogheda has been deepened. Even although the mussel beds have been extensively re-seeded by BIM there is some concern in the district that the deepening will have irreparably altered the flow regime in the estuary, making this ancient fishing method inoperable. As Leo Boyle points out, the flow rate of the ebb at three hours after high tide is now more like the previous flow rate at four and a half hours – the deeper the estuary, the lower the expected rate of flow – so there is every possibility that raking may no longer be feasible under the new conditions. The estuary will probably reopen for mussel fishing in 2004 and then it will become clear whether mussel raking can continue. Raking is an environmentally friendly and eminently sustainable way to collect mussels; the very uncertainty of the technique ensures that its impact on the stocks is less than that of modern power dredging. Whether the young people of the district will be keen to maintain the tradition, which requires skill and experience, is not at all certain. Its disappearance would end a long and unique tradition in Ireland. Strangely enough, this appears to be the first detailed description of the raking method as actually used for mussels in the Boyne. The technique died out long ago at Castlemaine in Co. Kerry, and at Wexford, and we do not know the exact details of how it was pursued in those non-estuarine sites. It will be ironic if this, the first detailed description of it, coincides with the final abandonment of this ancient and now unique style of fishing.

We started this chapter "crying cockles and mussels, alive alive-o" so let us end it with Darina Allen's way of presenting these two wonderful molluscs, outlined in the accompanying box.

Darina Allen's Cockles Or Mussels With Mayonnaise

Allow 12 per person
Cockles or mussels
Home made Mayonnaise
Garnish – Sprigs of fennel or flat parsley

Check that all the cockles or mussels are tightly shut. Wash them under lots of cold running water. Put them in a single layer in a wide frying pan. Cover with a folded tea-towel and cook on a gentle heat for 1-2 minutes. As soon as they open, remove the tea-towel. If you are using mussels, remove the beards and leave the mussels or cockles on a half shell. Allow them to get quite cold. Loosen the mussels or cockles from the shell, pipe a tiny rosette of mayonnaise on each one and decorate with a sprig of fennel or flat parsley.

MAYONNAISE

2 egg yolks, free range.
1½ teaspoon salt.
Pinch of English mustard or ½ teaspoon French mustard.
1 dessertspoon white wine vinegar.
8 fl ozs (250ml) oil (sunflower, arachide or olive oil or a mixture) - *we use 6 fl ozs (175ml) arachide oil and 2 fl ozs (50ml) olive oil, alternatively use 7/1*

Put the egg yolks into a bowl with the mustard, salt and the white wine vinegar. Put the oil into a measure. Take a whisk in one hand and the oil in the other and drip the oil onto the egg yolks, drop by drop whisking at the same time. Within a minute you will notice that the mixture is beginning to thicken. When this happens you can add the oil a little faster, but don't get too cheeky or it will suddenly curdle because the egg yolks can only absorb the oil at a certain pace. Taste and add a little more seasoning and vinegar if necessary.
If the Mayonnaise curdles it will suddenly become quite thin, and if left sitting the oil will start to float to the top of the sauce. If this happens you can quite easily rectify the situation by putting another egg yolk or 1-2 tablespoons of boiling water into a clean bowl, then whisk in the curdled Mayonnaise, a half teaspoon at a time until it emulsifies again. The great secret is to have all your ingredients at room temperature and to drip the oil very slowly into the egg yolks at the beginning. The quality of your Mayonnaise will depend totally on the quality of your egg yolks, oil and vinegar and it's perfectly possible to make a bland Mayonnaise if you use poor quality ingredients.

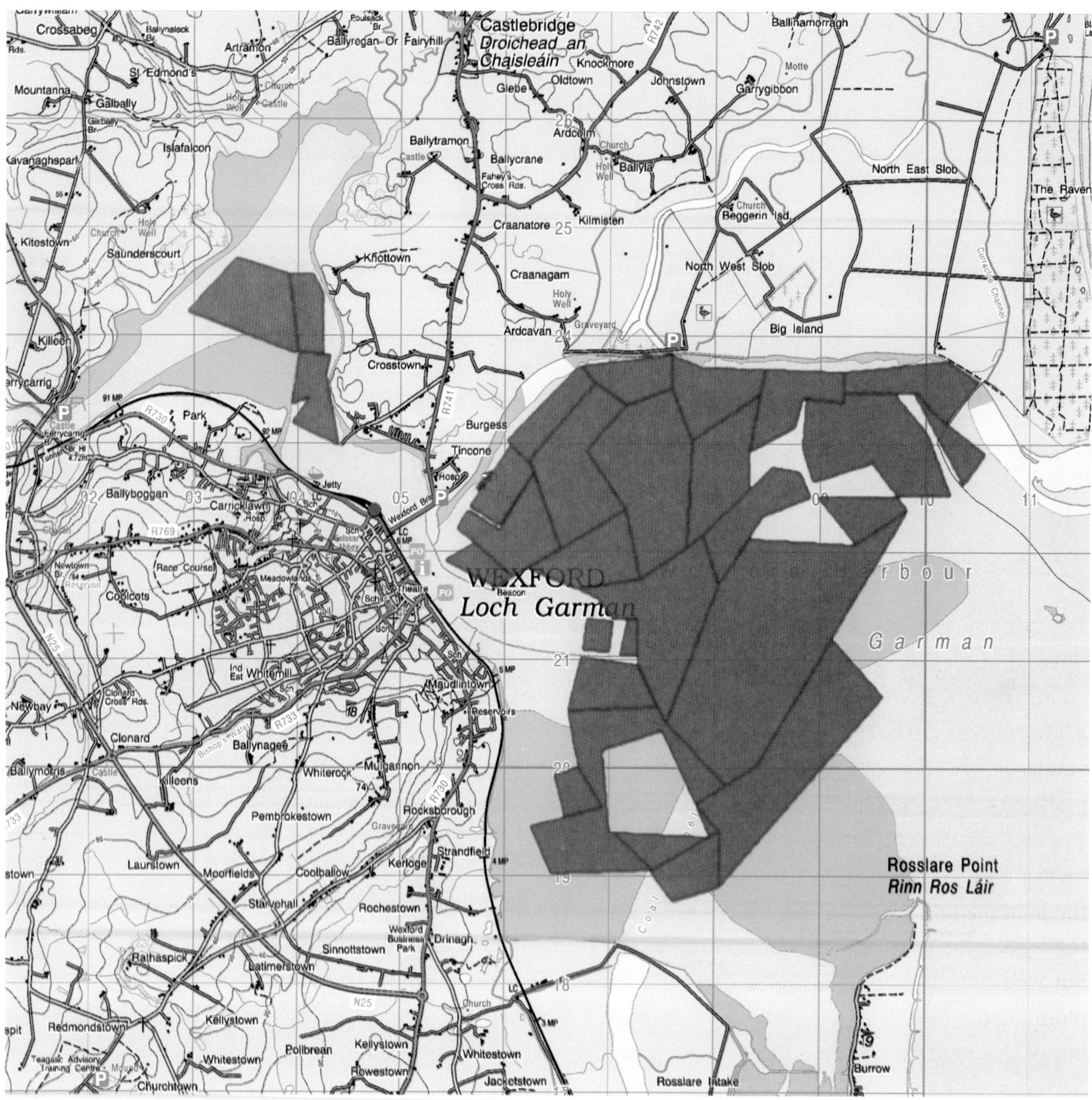

Fig. 28. Map indicating the underwater mussel plots in Wexford Harbour. Although rarely marked with buoys, the location of the different plots, which are allocated to different fishermen, are known to the participants in the fishery. Map courtesy of BIM.

Chapter 4

MUSSEL CULTURE

The mussel attaches itself to rocky ridges, rocks, buoys, the piles of piers and other hard bodies; it lives also in countless numbers on certain types of sandbanks known as "scalps" . . . Advantage is taken of this fact to construct artificial "scalps" where the natural do not occur. Several highly successful scalps have been made in France and Germany, and they supply thousands of tons of mussels to the enterprising "farmers".

Louis Renouf, *Animal Life on the Seashore, 1930.*

THE SUCCESSFUL PRODUCTION of any shellfish, whether wild or in culture, requires three things: recruitment, survival and growth. Recruitment is the entry of new young individuals to the stock each year to maintain and renew it by replacing the adults that are lost to the harvest or to natural mortality. The vast majority of the young is doomed to die, often at the hands or teeth of their neighbours. Nature is profligate in this matter and in order to maintain the stock it is necessary that only two individuals should survive to adulthood from the many millions produced by each adult pair. But what is a loss for one species is often a gain for another so that the James Bond title "Live and let die" is not altogether untrue or uncommon in the wild. Growth is the increase in size and weight of the animals as they age. But we do not want our shellfish simply to be big. We often want them to be plump and "meaty". So growth usually includes "fattening", that is, the bulking out of the adult's body when they have fed well. The environmental conditions necessary for these different aspects of life are not always the same.

Consider for a moment the life cycle of a typical bivalve. The adults produce and release into the water column many millions of larvae – many billions if the stock is large – each year. If all were to settle and survive close to their parents the density of individuals in that place would soon become impossibly enormous. The young would compete with their parents for food and space to the detriment of both. Individuals would not grow big and many would become stunted and misshapen or would not fatten over time. Therefore it suits the parents if the currents and tides take most of their larval offspring away to settle elsewhere. When the adults live in an area with strong tidal flow or strong currents the process of dispersing the larvae can be highly efficient. The very currents that sweep the larvae away are the same currents that bring in planktonic food to the parents, so a site that is good for feeding may also be one that is good for producing and dispersing larvae.

Because it may lose most of its own young by dispersion, an established population needs to gain new young recruits from elsewhere if it is to be maintained over generations. Exactly the same transport process that disperses their own offspring downstream brings in new larvae from upstream populations. So as we move down the current, each population can be a source population (provider of larvae) to a sink population (receiver of larvae) further downstream. A sink population may, in its turn, be a source population to one even further away and so on, source and sink populations alternating down the current or tidal course. The exact places where the larvae will settle after dispersion depend on the strength and direction of the transporting currents and the length of the larval life. For mussels this is usually thirty to sixty days. The exact number of larvae that eventually settle depends on their survival during dispersion and on the nature of the sea bottom where they arrive. Many never make it and many others never settle successfully, or die, or are killed after settlement. If a sink population occupies a poor growing area its survival will be poor and its larval output will consequently be lessened. At the end of the chain, there may be a final sink population whose larvae are swept away to unsuitable places or are lost by being carried out to the open sea far from settlement sites. In enclosed bays, on the other hand, the populations may form a kind of reproductive gyre, where they all exchange larvae between one another. This can happen in bays or long inlets where the tide oscillates and does not fully exchange with the open sea as frequently or as fully as normal. Killary Harbour is one example. Such a bay may then have a particularly high density of stocks (high recruitment), but it will be at severe risk of becoming depleted of its food by the sheer numbers of mouths to be fed. Each bay has a limited “carrying capacity” that cannot be exceeded.

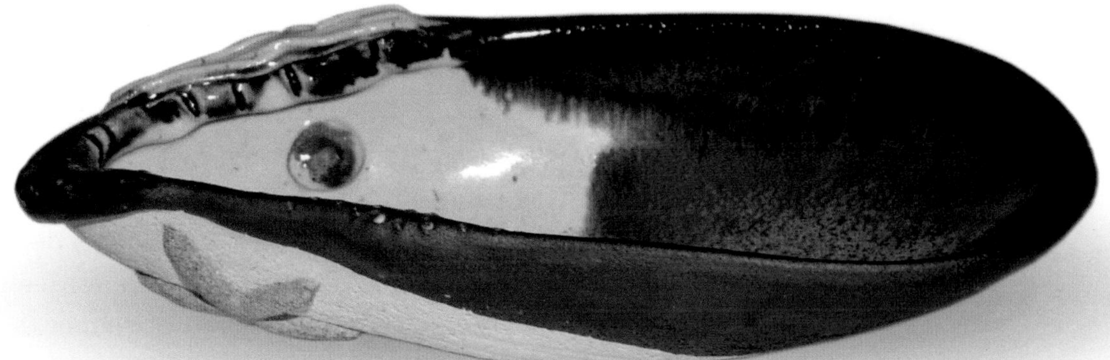

Fig. 29. The mussel was once described as having "a dark blue unattractive shell, shaped like a deep, squat boat". Jan Sell, who designed and made this ceramic bowl, would hardly agree that the mussel shell is unattractive.

So, nature has provided a sophisticated and efficient means whereby wild populations can renew themselves with recruits from other, often unrelated, wild populations. This sustains the genetic and environmental health of the stocks but countless numbers of larvae and spat are lost in the process. Harvesting of wild mussels is the cropping of such adult populations at levels that do not impact negatively on the ability of the stocks to regenerate themselves. Artificial mussel cultivation, in contrast, sets out to gather and rear some of the billions of larvae, or the small spat, that would otherwise be lost to natural mortality. Generally speaking, when the spat are gathered and taken elsewhere for managed cultivation on the sea bottom it is called "bottom culture" of mussels. When larvae or spat are harvested with a view to growing them on ropes or in plastic mesh the process is called "suspended culture" of mussels.

It is a very small step from traditional harvesting to bottom culture, which really only involves making the best use of the different kinds of ground available to the producer. From time immemorial oysters, for instance, have been cultured by transplantation from good spatting grounds to good growing grounds and by transfer from one growing bed to another as growth and fattening conditions dictated. The Romans had done this very successfully two thousand years ago and probably others before them had done it too. The first recorded transplantation of oysters into Ireland was in 1614 when Sir Thomas Colclough imported seed oysters from Milford Haven in Wales to Bannow Bay in County Wexford. If bottom culture worked so well with oysters, why not with mussels? The principle of the method was simple and well known but the need for bottom culture in Ireland only arose when the supply of wild mussels failed to meet the increasing demands on them in recent times.

Wexford Harbour was one of the first Irish localities where the local wild mussel stocks became seriously depleted. Fortunately there were large stocks of mussels outside Wexford Harbour and the custom arose of dredging the small mussels from there and re-laying them on the depleted inner Harbour beds to grow. That way the recruitment problem was solved and the small transplanted seed mussels could grow well in the more sheltered Harbour where conditions for growth were good. This ensured the continued reputation of Wexford for mussels. Initially all the imported seed was dredged from areas close by. With time these areas too became depleted and the dredgers had to go further afield for seed supplies. By then it was known that great banks of small mussels occurred in the Irish Sea off the coasts of Counties Wicklow and Wexford. These were to become the source of seed not only for Wexford Harbour but also for elsewhere in Ireland in the last decade.

Once any shellfish is transplanted and laid down on the sea bottom elsewhere, "Went's worry", as I call it in a later chapter, comes into play. That is, there may be nothing to stop any person from freely dredging the transplanted stock, without legal let or hindrance. Indeed, Common Law may even defend the stranger's right to do just that. What was needed if bottom culture were to thrive was a system that guaranteed that the re-laid stock was protected from the depredations of others. "Mussel Orders" and an Aquaculture Licensing Scheme were introduced to meet this difficulty. About twelve hundred hectares of Wexford Harbour were designated as mussel culture ground and allocated for use exclusively by the local mussel cooperative. The ground was subdivided into sections or patches, rather like fields on the land, and eleven syndicates seeded and cultivated their own allocated sections. In 2001, when over 12,000 tonnes of seed were brought in from the Irish Sea beds, they were scattered over about 650 hectares at an average density of 20 tonnes per hectare. The remaining ground, about 500 hectares, was kept aside for the growth of maturing mussels brought in at other times. The "fields" are fixed on maps of the Harbour (Fig. 28) and although there are rarely any buoys to mark them their location is known to the various interested parties. Buoys and other markers could hinder navigation in the Harbour and are therefore not really desirable. About 7,000 tonnes of full-grown mussels were landed and sold in 2001, bringing in a healthy 4 million euro at first sale and giving employment to almost forty men. About 10,000 tonnes are estimated to be the optimum amount of mussels that can be produced sustainably in Wexford Harbour, so the industry there is working at nearly 70% of the optimum. It certainly is a valuable addition to the economy and the exports of the town.

At Cromane, Castlemaine, a similar structured division of the available ground between the members of the Fishery Cooperative was introduced in the 1990s. About 180 hectares of intertidal nursery and sub-tidal growing ground were divided among seventeen producer syndicates, all the members of a syndicate being members of the Fishery Cooperative. Here too the ground was subdivided into "fields" or "pitches". In 2001, only about 30% of the ground was cultivated with 12% of that under seed and the remainder allocated to larger maturing mussels. Unlike Wexford, some of the ground is intertidal and that is used as nursery ground for the young seed. Seed mussels of five to twenty-five millimetres in size are dredged from deeper "spatfall" areas locally and transplanted to the allocated intertidal nurseries where they grow for twelve to eighteen months. Thereafter they are moved to the subtidal plots where they remain until final harvesting at market size normally a year or two later. Each syndicate manages its own production plots, the Cooperative acting only to regulate the overall issues of ground allocation, conservation actions and disputes.

What was virtually an abandoned resource has now been transformed by the introduction of bottom cultivation. Landings have increased remarkably in recent years (1999 was an exception), so much so that no fewer than nine large dredgers were working the area in year 2000 when 2,500 tonnes of marketable mussels were landed. The harvest in 2001 was just less than that but it brought in nearly one million euro. About 8,000 tonnes of seed mussels are needed each year to stock the plots adequately. A development plan for the area estimates that mussel output can increase to 12,000 tonnes a year on a sustainable basis, so the enterprise there is still a long way from saturation.

Only on one occasion ever was it necessary to bring in seed from the Irish Sea to augment the local supply and that did not prove very successful. New seedbeds were located in 1994 just outside the cultivated zone and these now contribute the extra seed needed for the Harbour so that the area is fully self-sufficient. This is a most satisfactory state as it makes Cromane independent of the much-abused Irish Sea stocks. It is estimated that about 30,000 tonnes of seed mussels have been transplanted in Cromane since 1994 and a similar weight of market-sized mussels has been landed. We must remember that a tonne of seed mussels contains many more individuals than a tonne of fully-grown mussels. Natural mortality is huge on mussel beds, both wild and cultivated. Starfish and crabs are the great killers and between them they can wipe out a stock in very short time. A starfish opens the mussel (or any other shellfish it happens upon) with its strong sticky arms and then everts its stomach into the gaping shell and digests the victim. In bottom culture, the growers try to remove starfish by "mopping". For this, a boat or dredger draws an old hempen net or large bundle of old rope over the ground. The starfish become entangled in it and are raised to the surface where they are killed. Crabs prefer smaller mussels that they can crush easily with their claws. The growers set pots to gather the crabs as best they can but the task seems to go on and on.

Bottom culture of mussels is now practiced in many other areas where the local natural stocks are not sufficiently productive on their own. The important centres are Clew Bay, Lough Foyle and Waterford Estuary. All of these receive seed, to a greater or lesser extent, from the Irish Sea and sometimes from other areas where there is an excess. Lough Foyle is the largest of the bottom-mussel production areas with an output of 9,000 tonnes in 2001. This required an input of about 21,000 tonnes of seed mussels, almost one third of which was dredged and transported from the Irish Sea beds. Over sixty people are engaged in the business, which is valued at over 3 million euro at first sale. Taking the country as a whole, over 20,000 tonnes of fully-grown bottom mussels were produced with a value of more than 10 million euro in 2001. For this, 53,000 tonnes of seed mussels were transplanted of which 32,000 tonnes (60%) came from the Irish Sea seedbeds. Estimates of the seed requirements for later years are significantly in excess of these amounts.

From all this it will be obvious that the Irish Sea provides an enormous quantity of natural seed to the industry. One estimate suggests that upwards of one thousand tonnes are taken each night during the summer season from the Irish Sea and a total allowable catch of 98,000 tonnes a year is now in force. Alarm bells are already starting to sound. These Irish Sea banks are the ones that held "inexhaustible" stocks of oysters in the nineteenth century. We may find, when we have fished them out, that the mussel stocks are similarly "inexhaustible". It will be too late to do much if we wait until a marked decline in output becomes established. At very least the situation needs constant monitoring and a proper plan for the balanced use of this unique but finite national resource is warranted.

Fig. 30. A navigation buoy, cleaned, painted and ready to go back into the sea. Within a few months the base of a buoy like this is covered with a dense coat of mussels.

Fig. 31. The first generation of mussel culture used rafts like these to suspend the mussel ropes. These are the last three such rafts remaining in Killary Harbour.

All the indications that mussels were easy to culture in suspension in the water column were obvious to Irish observers from very early on. William Thompson, a noted Irish naturalist of the day, recorded that in 1843 a Captain M'Kibbin described to him how a newly-cleaned navigation buoy (Fig. 30), when placed in the sea, was soon covered a foot thick with mussels around the entire circumference of its base to a depth of one foot. He estimated they weighed half a ton. Thompson went on to say: "The bases of these buoys in our bay [Belfast Lough] become at once covered with mussels; those one year down, on being examined, are covered with them of about half the full-grown size and those two years down do not [yet] display them of full size . . . The mussels on the buoys are considered to be of a very superior quality, and have the great advantage of being quite free from sand, the water washing round them, keeping them quite pure." When the mussels were full-grown they "were carried away by persons to eat." All the ingredients for a successful suspended-culture mussel industry – from putting out clean collectors, monitoring growth over time, observing the superior quality of the mussels and having a ready market for them – were present in Thompson's short account. But in the mid-nineteenth century there was no shortage of wild mussels and there was no need for any artificial cultivation. Thompson's observations were not to be the beginning of the Irish suspended-culture mussel industry any more than Walton's were.

The modern industry was in fact adapted from the culture system in use since the 1940s in the *rias* of Galicia in northern Spain. There, timber rafts supported by floats and secured by anchors were used to suspend long ropes on which the mussels were fixed and grown (Fig 31). Seed mussels were scraped from the rocks at low tide and attached by hand to the ropes. To do this they were placed in long mesh tubes ("stockings") that were then bound to the ropes. As they grew the mussels pushed out through the mesh and re-distributed themselves along the rope. They needed to be thinned every so often because the mass of mussels soon became too heavy for a single rope to hold. The "thinnings" were in turn placed in new stockings and bound to further ropes where they continued their growth. This straightforward but effective system enabled the mussel culture industry of Galicia to grow to almost 300,000 tonnes annually and it is little wonder that countries like Ireland decided to emulate the successful Spanish experience.

Experimental suspended-culture of mussels in Ireland was attempted first in Connemara. Irish conditions are not exactly like those in the *rias* and the early trials proved that things were not as simple as they might have seemed. The mass of mussels that any raft and any individual rope was capable of holding was found to be critical, not only for the stability and buoyancy of the raft itself but also for the successful growth of the mussels. When they were too dense they either fell off the ropes and were lost or they grew poorly. Inserting timber battens through the lay of the ropes at intervals of a few inches or so could solve the first. That stabilized the mussel masses and prevented them from slipping off. But the growth was poorest on those ropes hanging towards the centre of the raft, suggesting that the availability of sufficient food was the problem there. Never the less, the early trials were sufficiently successful to warrant commercialisation of the enterprise.

Fig. 32. The local community in Bantry responded creatively to the development of mussel cultivation. Here an enterprising local offers free mussels to passing motorists while humourously mimicking in print the local Cork accent. Imaginative gestures like this encourage people to try out what may sometimes be seen as "exotic" seafood. "Dat's right, boy – de're free!"

While the new culture technology spread to all coastal areas, nowhere was the response to it as positive as it was in Bantry Bay. Mussel culture caught the imagination of the local community (Fig 32) and within a few years Bantry Bay became the undoubted and undisputed centre of suspended mussel culture in Ireland. It was indeed fortunate that so many were attracted to the new enterprise: only large operations can guarantee the security of supply that customers, especially customers abroad, demand. The new mussel ventures in the west of Ireland were individually too small at that time to make any real impact in trade. By organising their activities the individual growers in Bantry Bay generated the critical mass that allowed the industry to take off and ultimately to thrive. This was not achieved without setbacks, difficulties and some painful experiences.

Hard commercial realities regarding supply, product quality and pricing had to be learned in Bantry where mussels had until then been used only as fertilizer for growing potatoes. Bantry is still the centre of the suspended-culture industry with modern processing facilities that underpin the continued development of the production units. Bantry Bay Seafoods, the main mussel processor in Ireland, now take in mussels from suspended-culture and from bottom-culture enterprises all over the country and even from producers abroad.

Mussels grown in suspended-culture spend all their lives hanging about. Ideally, the wild spat are collected on hanging ropes suspended in the water at the time of natural settlement during the summer. For this to be successful it is necessary for the grower to be able to predict with some accuracy the expected days of settlement. Then the ropes can be deployed to best advantage at the appropriate time. Deployed too early, the ropes will be host to other unwanted settlers like sea squirts and barnacles, fouling organisms that can add enormously to the difficulty of successful mussel culture. Deployed too late, the mussel settlement may be missed altogether. Shellfish farmers observe the plankton for the presence and abundance of mussel larvae in order to anticipate the likely time of settlement. Collecting ropes are then deployed. Once the larvae have settled the ropes are removed to the growing site and attached permanently to the floatation device. As growth progresses the mussels are thinned and redistributed on new ropes to reduce their density and to ensure proper access to food for all.

Fig. 33. A line of floats in Killary Harbour marks a mussel farm. This system of floats in a line replaced the old rafts and is regarded as visually much less intrusive.

Fig. 34. Colourful buoys, recycled drums originally used to carry fruit juice, indicate the extent of mussel cultivation in Kilmacillogue Harbour, at the base of Knockatee Mountain in Co. Kerry. To some the scene is unattractive, to others it indicates a vibrant community making sustainable use of the marine resource to give local employment.

Fig. 35. Neat lines of modern, mostly gray coloured, buoys mark a mussel farm in Killary Harbour. Shellfish farmers are making determined efforts to make their enterprises visually less obvious.

The use of rafts as platforms for rope suspension lasted only a few years. They are not particularly suited to the exposed nature of many of our coasts and they tend to break up easily in stormy conditions. Because the mussels set on ropes suspended towards the centre of the raft grew poorly, it was thought better to suspend the ropes from long head-lines that are supported by buoys or floats, doing away with the raft altogether. In practice, two ropes stretching in long parallel lines join together a series of large floats (Fig. 33). At first recycled drums, previously used to transport fruit juice, were the preferred floats as they were easily available. Being relatively inexpensive and highly coloured they were regarded as a cheap and cheerful solution to the floatation problem. Not everyone however appreciated their visual impact, especially in the remoter, more "touristy" areas (Fig. 34). It is an inescapable fact of life that human enterprise impacts on the environment and on occasions actually enhances it. The sight of shellfish enterprises is welcomed by many people as a sign of an appropriate and sustainable use of our natural resources, no more objectionable than any other well-managed resource-based activity. However, when custom-made floats became available later on, it was considered prudent to make them in muted grey tones that are said to be more in tune or in tone with the colours of the Irish seascape. In small, unintended ways like this we send mixed messages about our climate and weather to intending tourist visitors.

The lines of floats, of whatever colour (Fig. 35), are moored at both ends with heavy anchors. To these head ropes, weighted ropes called "droppers" are attached (Figs. 36 and 37). The droppers are the mussel-bearing ropes and are

normally about nine or ten metres in length, each rope having small timber battens inserted into its lay at intervals of about twenty centimetres. A fully laden rope can carry a maximum of about nine kilograms of mussels but four or five kilograms is more common (Fig. 38). Growth to market size takes up to two years after which the ropes are raised and the mussels are harvested. After grading, the large mussels are packed for sale and the small ones are put into mesh (pergolari) stockings and re-attached to new ropes to continue their growth (Fig. 39).

Sites like Ardgroom and Killary Harbour have sufficient larval densities to permit the collection of all the necessary seed on ropes suspended in the water. Spat settle most densely at a depth of around five metres from the surface, so special droppers are used for collection. Ten-metre lengths of rope are coiled into

Fig. 36. Floats support two parallel lines called head ropes at intervals. Lighter ropes called "droppers" hang from the head ropes and the mussels are attached to these. A dropper rope is about 10 metres long and each holds about 5 kg of growing mussels.

Fig. 37. A boat servicing mussel lines in Killary Harbour. A powered winch lifts the floats and head ropes out of the water. This raises the vertical dropper ropes that are coated in mussels. The droppers can then be detached from the head rope and the dropper and mussels are passed along a conveyor belt to the grading machine on board. New dropper ropes may be attached before the head rope is released back into the sea. The boat then moves on to another section of head rope and repeats the process.

Fig. 38. Two dropper ropes covered with half-grown mussels.

Fig. 39. Filling a mesh stocking with young mussels. Mussels on the upper platform are fed through a narrow pipe into the vertical stocking held by the operator beneath the platform. When ready, the stocking is attached to a fresh dropper rope that is then attached to a floating head rope.

loose loops and these coils are attached to short ropes so as to hang at depths from three to seven metres. This increases the surface area in the critical layer for attachment of the spat. When the coils have been adequately settled they are removed, uncoiled and then hung as normal droppers at the growing site. In some areas the density of wild larvae is not adequate, or its settlement days cannot be predicted with sufficient accuracy, to enable the numbers needed by the growers to be collected on ropes. In that case wild mussel spat is gathered from the rocks by scraping off the natural settlement (Fig. 40), called "rock mussel" and removing it to the ropes. It is attached, either by bandaging it onto the ropes using biodegradable cotton bandages or by placing it in plastic mesh tubes that are then wound onto the ropes. One might expect that once an industry matures in a bay there will be adequate supplies of spat to meet its needs, coming partly from the offspring of those mussels that fall from the ropes and successfully grow on the bottom and partly from early spawning of the rope mussels themselves. If a mature enterprise must continue to rely for recruits each year on wild spat settling naturally on rocks, it suggests that the industry may not be as secure in its recruitment as one would like.

When we consider the two kinds of mussel production – bottom culture and suspended culture – together, we see a startling paradox. That is, on the one hand the localised shortage of wild spat for the bottom culture industry that necessitates excessive recourse to the wild mussel beds of the Irish Sea and on the other, the simultaneous excess of spat available to many local suspended-culture enterprises. At Ardgroom for example, John Harrington is trying to *reduce* the density of spat settling on the ropes to the optimum that can be grown efficiently to the adult stage. New forms of collector, made of a kind of webbing material disposed in a continuous belt that can be easily lifted after limited settlement has occurred, are proving useful for this. Generally speaking, mussel spat settling on ropes is not regarded as suitable for seeding the bottom culture areas and bottom-cultured mussels do not thrive in suspended culture. We must remember that all the mussels are members of the same species and the differences between the spat in the different culture methods are unlikely to be fundamental. A great advance would be to devise nursery protocols whereby the excess of the suspended culture industry could be made suitable for bottom cultivation, thus relieving the demand on the Irish Sea stocks. It is very likely that spat of one source can be acclimated fairly easily to conditions in the other. Experiments on this could well be pursued at sites like the disused depuration tanks at Cromane. There can be no certainty of sustainability where security of recruitment is not guaranteed and progress with this would represent a really important advance for the industry.

Dealers and consumers also distinguish between bottom-cultured and suspended-cultured mussels. The former have a higher meat yield and are normally sold live and unprocessed, mainly to the Dutch market. The latter are much better suited to processing and they form the raw material for the rapidly expanding processed mussel trade. When natural rock mussel seed is used in suspended-culture, as happens in Bantry Bay, the resultant adult mussels tend to have higher meat yields but slightly more brittle shells. In Clew Bay, where mussels were known traditionally as "blackshells", both kinds of mussel culture are practiced so that maximum use is made of the extensive grade A waters available in that wonderful water body. What all this signifies is that we are still a long way from fully understanding all the factors that determine the yield and quality of mussels in any given area.

Fig. 40. A sheet of mussels covering intertidal rocks on the coast of Connemara. Mussel seed like this is sometimes used to supply the suspended mussel cultivation industry wherever sufficient spat is not readily available.

Galway Bay Mussels and Spaghetti

INGREDIENTS

1 kg mussels. 2 tbl. spoons olive oil. Spaghetti for two persons. 4 cloves garlic.
3-4 smoked rashers. 2 medium onions. 2 tbl. spoons crème fraiche. Salt and pepper.
Herbs: marjoram, thyme, oregano, parsley.
Optional: 1 medium courgette and/or 3-4 organic tomatoes.

METHOD

Cook mussels in covered saucepan without water for about 5 minutes and set aside to cool. Cut rashers into small cubes and brown in a saucepan with olive oil. Add crushed garlic and finely cut onions and sweat for 5 – 10 minutes. Add the optional, finely cut courgettes and/or tomatoes. Remove mussels from their shells and add to above. Add salt, pepper and chopped herbs. Remove from heat and add the crème fraiche. Serve over cooked spaghetti.

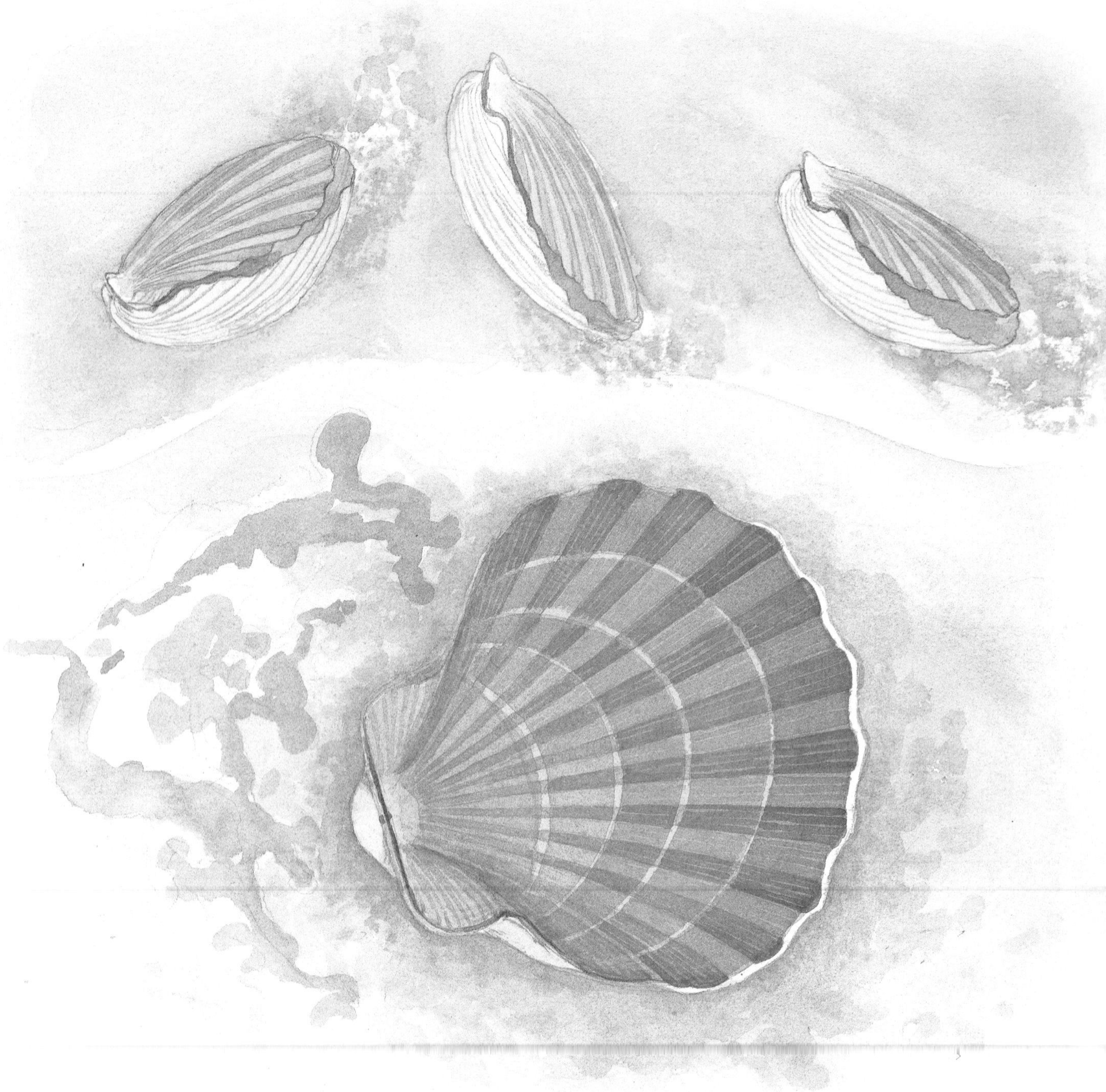

Chapter 5

SCALLOPS
THE KINGS AND QUEENS OF MOLLUSCS

The most esteemed of all the shell-fish tribe
by the western fishermen is the scallop.

W. H. Maxwell, *Wild Sports of the West, 1850.*

THE TERM "SCALLOP" COVERS MORE than 300 separate but related species distributed all over the world. In Ireland three species are common and they are the royalty of Irish shellfish. The King or Great scallop is *Pecten maximus*, known in Irish as *an muirín*; a sister species, *Chlamys opercularis* is known as the Queen scallop. The least common species, *Chlamys varia,* is called the variegated scallop, known in the Kinvara district of Galway as *an frithidín*. Elsewhere the latter two are not normally distinguished in the Irish language, both rejoicing in the name *an cluaisín*. This Irish word means "a little ear" and refers to the fact that in both these species one of the ears of the shell is larger than the other. These species are also smaller than the King scallop.

Never among shellfish was the epithet "royal" so richly merited both in life, in art and in gastronomy. Scallops are lively animals given to swimming freely when disturbed or when threatened by enemies. Some can move at speeds up to 4 kilometres per hour. Most species move around less as they get older, just like humans. All other bivalve species, except for the razorfish, are relatively sedentary and do not move in the water column once they have passed the larval dispersal stage. The fact that the scallops' mode of progression has been likened to a parade of false teeth – by rapidly opening and closing of the shells in a snapping motion they execute a form of jerky jet propulsion – makes little of the complexity of their locomotion and its importance in predator avoidance.

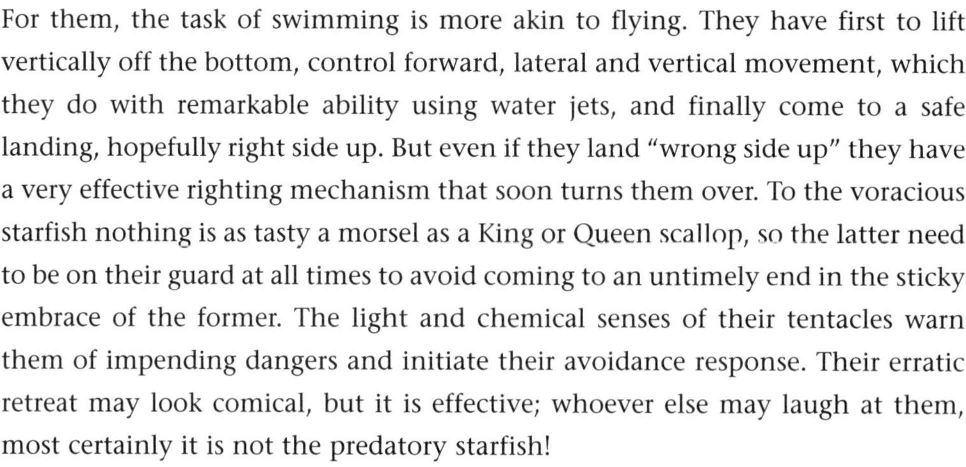

For them, the task of swimming is more akin to flying. They have first to lift vertically off the bottom, control forward, lateral and vertical movement, which they do with remarkable ability using water jets, and finally come to a safe landing, hopefully right side up. But even if they land "wrong side up" they have a very effective righting mechanism that soon turns them over. To the voracious starfish nothing is as tasty a morsel as a King or Queen scallop, so the latter need to be on their guard at all times to avoid coming to an untimely end in the sticky embrace of the former. The light and chemical senses of their tentacles warn them of impending dangers and initiate their avoidance response. Their erratic retreat may look comical, but it is effective; whoever else may laugh at them, most certainly it is not the predatory starfish!

Fig. 41. Holy water font in St. Francis Church (the Abbey), Galway City. Note the shell decoration. By tradition, Galwegians touch the face of St. Claire whenever they use the font. This accounts for the face worn smooth and darkened by the touch of generations of believers.

Scallops made the earliest, the most prestigious and the longest lasting appearance of all shellfish in works of art. Botticelli's Birth of Aphrodite is, perhaps, the most celebrated depiction of the scallop and one of remarkable realism. In it, the shell is not simply decorative but allegorically expressive of the mythology surrounding the Goddess. The mythological association of Aphrodite and the shell dates from about the fifth century B.C. and the shell came to symbolise the sea itself in Hellenic art. In classical architecture, the scallop motif became widely used to decorate the roofs of niches (small alcoves) dedicated to various deities. Indeed, the scallop shape is particularly suited to the half-dome structure of the niche, so much so that it is not clear even to the experts whether, in most instances, the scallop decoration is simply an easy sculptural decoration or has a more recondite meaning. In other words, does the scallop simply fit the niche or did the niche evolve from the scallop? Which came first, the scallop or the niche? Whatever the answer, the scallop niche appears to have been the classical forerunner of features like the Queen Ann shell porch in architecture. In Ireland the scallop motif is expressed classically in the fanlight tracery of some Georgian doorways in Dublin and in the shell masques of certain Irish Georgian side tables. Its use in a holy water font is shown in Fig. 41.

As well as being particularly decorative the scallop shell is particularly useful in other contexts too. It had many functions in the Roman dining room as a container for eggs, fish, oil and fruit and in the boudoir to hold oils and unguents. It makes a handy scoop or measure and was a common open container used for many purposes. In Ireland it had a traditional function in illumination. Filled with seal or shark oil and bearing a peeled rush spill as a wick, it made a functioning crusie lamp, the only source of light in the dark homes of the rural poor long ago. Such lamps were hung in, or near, the hearth partly to waft the pungent smell of the burning fish oil up the chimney and partly because that was where life indoors was lived. And in the night, as the *seanachie* weaved his magic with words, unfolding in resonant phrases the deeds of heroic men and tempting goddesses, who knows what alluring creatures were conjured up in the minds of his listeners by the flickering, luminous flame rising from the shell? What Venus was given flesh, what Aphrodite was given form, what fairy queen was released to steal away a chosen child? Classical imagery was no stranger to the imaginings of even the most ordinary people in the old Irish culture that was so rich in storytelling and oral tradition. Scallop shells as a source of light continued in use in the Aran Islands until recent memory, when the paraffin lamp finally displaced them. Nowadays, the *seanachies* are no more, the Aran Islands are lit and powered by electricity and scallop shells are more associated with a certain commercial brand of mineral oil.

Almost as an antidote to their association with opulent art and architecture, scallops became the symbol of St. James and of penitential pilgrimages in the middle ages. Some would hold that the idea of graduated penances involving fasting and pilgrimages was a peculiarly Irish invention brought to Europe by monks in the Dark Ages. A long and arduous pilgrimage was indeed a typical example of the Irish penance of exile – the Irish always exile those who oppose or upset the prevailing authority – and it was a sentence liberally dispensed for great sins by the Irish monks. The Irish church was certainly austere at that time and maybe Europe needed the discipline the Irish provided. A pilgrimage would normally be made to the Holy Land, or to the tombs of the martyrs in Rome or to the shrines of particular saints. Lough Derg in Co. Donegal, known as St. Patrick's Purgatory, was a popular pilgrim destination in medieval Ireland as it still is today. But, Rome apart, the most popular pilgrimage destination in Europe was the shrine of St. James at Santiago di Compostela in Spain.

Fig. 42. Effigy of St. James on a late 15th century tomb in the Franciscan friary at Kilconnell Co. Galway. Note the scallop shells on his purse and hat. In this sculpture the saint has a rather mischievous grin, as if he knew that the name of the tomb's occupant would be forgotten (as it has) while his own name would remain.

Fig. 43. An old friar (on the left) who has completed the pilgrimage to Santiago di Compostella reads a blessing to a young friar about to set out on his journey. The older one has a scallop shell on his habit, the younger holds a staff for the impending journey. The monument, by Genesis Fine Arts, is located in Mullingar Co. Westmeath and commemorates the local Augustinian Priory of St. Mary where several scallop shells were excavated along with the bones of monks from its 16th century graveyard.

In the twelfth century the scallop became particularly associated with the person and the shrine of St. James. Because of this it became known as *coquille San Jacques* or, in modern America, St. James' cockle. It adorns the statues and pictures of the saint from that century on, often attached to his hat (James is the only Apostle normally depicted with headgear) or on his pilgrim's scrip (his purse or *sparán*) (Fig. 42). Very quickly the scallop shell was adopted as the universal symbol of the penitential pilgrim irrespective of his origin or destination (Fig. 43). Precisely why this association arose is not at all clear but the shell's sheer usefulness and versatility as a bowl, a plate, a scoop, and a measure must have been a boon to the humble pilgrim who was travelling light and carrying nothing but his sins and what he wore. Since pilgrimages involved hardship and suffering this association redeemed the scallop motif from the symbol of privilege and decadence it might otherwise have taken on through its other high art associations.

Scallops occur all over Ireland but usually in rather limited beds. The main areas in which they are harvested are the bays of southwest Cork and Kerry from Schull to Valentia, the inlets of the north shore of Galway Bay and Mulroy Bay in County Donegal. Elsewhere they occur in smaller numbers that can sustain local harvesting but which are not normally sufficient for sustained commercial fishing. The beds usually lie in waters from 2 to 20 fathoms deep, but off the coasts of Waterford and Wexford there are deep-water beds accessible only by boat and requiring powerful dredging equipment.

Occasionally scallops were gathered straight from the shore during exceptionally low tides, but the traditional method of gathering them from under water was by "shading" and the skilled use of the "*brideóg*". This is a hand net consisting of a larch pole, usually more than 20 feet in length, with a metal ring, about nine inches in diameter, attached to one end. A small-mesh net was lashed to the ring. The fisherman used a homemade device, such as a cutaway biscuit tin or a bottom-less bucket, to "shade" the sea bottom and to observe the scallop. King scallops lie flat with the saucer-shaped lower shell buried in the substrate up to the level of the upper shell. Where the lower shell overlaps the upper, a white gleam can be seen and this betrays the position of the scallop to the observer. The fisherman then lowered the *brideóg* and deftly struck the edge of the shellfish, tipping it from its seating so that it flipped over the rim of the ring into the net. To do this required great skill. The long pole was necessary, not to work deep water, but to provide a counter-weight that allowed the immersed part, usually about eight feet, to be manipulated easily. (Just try to make a fast, accurate stab with a long pole entirely under water and see how difficult it is!) In Valentia Harbour in Kerry, it was men from the Árd Cais part of the mainland who mostly fished this way. They did not use any shading device; on clear, still, frosty mornings around Christmas, when the sea was glassy calm, they would set about fishing and it was a poor day if they failed to gather 10 to 20 dozen scallops! The technique needed keen eyesight, a steady hand, good judgement of distance and a really calm sea. However, it is not as dangerous, for example, as the traditional method used to catch lobsters in Kerry. In this, one man jumped overboard and his companion held him down under the water with an oar until he had captured his prey! It is little wonder that using the *brideóg* has gone out of fashion, being replaced by the powered dredge while lobster pots have replaced the diving Kerry fishermen.

Before powered boats, scallop dredgers used either oars or sails or a kedging rope for dredging. Sail dredgers dragged the dredge – a sledge-like metal frame with a net attached (Fig. 44) – along the bottom as they progressed under wind power, sometimes augmented by rowing. Every so often the dredge was shipped and the contents of the net turned into the boat for sorting. The dredge was then shot again and the work continued. The technique of kedging, called scoping in Galway Bay, is fully described in chapter 7. It involved hauling the boat and the

Fig. 44. A traditional Irish dredge. The mouth is a rectangular metal frame to which the bag is attached (here only a piece of the bag is in place). The towing rope attaches to the ring at the top of the inclined metal arms. The bottom edge of the frame is called the blade or sword. It scrapes along the sea bottom, scooping the shells into the bag. Sometimes metal teeth are welded to the blade, especially when it is used for scallops.

dredge forward by pulling on an anchored rope, a really demanding, backbreaking, hand-chafing way of fishing. At Valentia, the fishermen would construct a temporary gantry, lashed to a thwart in the middle of the boat, on which the anchor rope was wound using a crank thereby making the task slightly less onerous. So it was a real godsend when outboard motors and eventually powered winches were introduced to the fisheries in the 1960s. With these, a much larger dredge could be towed at will and shipped by winch, making the fishing far easier and much more efficient. The catch, too, increased and 20 to 30 dozen scallops a day was not an unusual catch. Nowadays, all the boats are powered and the natural stocks are under severe threat of exhaustion. The fishing season is the period from October to April and the animals spawn and settle during the summer period. Serious efforts are underway to restock the Valentia beds with juvenile scallops.

Strangely enough, scallops were not universally popular as food all over the country. In some places, like Mulroy Bay, they were abundant but fished only seldom. In contrast, they were very much sought after as food in Dingle where they fetched six to eight pence a dozen in 1836. Near Dublin and elsewhere around the coast they were abundant but were used only as bait for cod and haddock fishing. Their use as bait for a different prey was given an interesting twist in County Mayo. According to Maxwell in his "Wild Sports of the West" ". . . [Scallops] are estimated so highly as a luxury as to cause their being transferred to the next gentleman who may have been serviceable to the peasant who finds them, or whose future favour it may be advisable to propitiate . . ." Maxwell regarded Mayo scallops as very superior in size and flavour and they, along with cockles and oysters, were certainly very abundant in Achill if he is to be believed.

Scallop beds are characteristically small and therefore particularly vulnerable to over-fishing. For a long time there has been a size limit of four and a half inches and individuals below that size may not be landed legally. The animals themselves are not very tolerant of cold conditions (their preferred temperature range is 9 to 17 degrees Celsius) and mortality can be massive in particularly cold winters like that of 1962/63. That year the stocks of the north shore of Galway Bay, which normally contributed half of the total Irish output, were almost completely wiped out and they are still only recovering. Irish output varied around 500,000 scallops a year (about 100 tonnes) with some exceptionally good and bad years, from early in the twentieth century until the last decade when they increased dramatically, and probably unsustainably, to 1,500 tonnes. Natural scallop spat settlement is characterised by rather large year-to-year fluctuations; this is reflected in the large fluctuations in landings giving a general unpredictability to the trade. Scallops are valuable on the European markets – the price in 2001 was 3,750 Euro a tonne – and competition is low, Ireland and the UK being the main suppliers. This, if ever, is an excellent candidate for aquaculture.

Here it is appropriate to ask how any species of marine animal first comes to be cultivated? The transit from harvesting to cultivation takes the same trajectory in most cases and it is based on the wonderful fecundity of the animals themselves. Most marine species are almost unbelievably fecund. In some, each female produces a superabundance, often many millions, of eggs. As discussed earlier, in order for any population no matter how large to maintain itself over generations all that is needed is that two individuals (on average) should survive from the millions of offspring of each spawning female. If more than that survive the population increases. If less, the population goes into decline. It follows that the vast majority of the offspring produced must die while they are still very young. Many never develop; many are swept away to unsuitable places; other animals eat many more; many fail to settle in the right places or are otherwise destroyed in the great struggle of life. But if the young can be collected while they are still in the earliest stage of life it may be possible to rear them under protected conditions so that a greater proportion of them will survive to the adult stage. This is what aquaculture does in its first phase. The aquaculturist collects the natural larvae or the spat present in the plankton after the wild adults have spawned. The spat settle and attach to hard surfaces some weeks after they have hatched from the eggs. So the aquaculturist needs only to provide plenty of suitable settlement surfaces, called collectors, to which the settling spat can attach. Then when they have attached, he removes the collectors to the hatchery (or nursery as it is now properly called) where he carefully removes the settled spat and places them in containers in which they can be fed a diet of suitable algae. Many of them thrive under these benign conditions. Many, of course, do not. But if only 1% survive of the many millions that are collected, then the operation is worth it and the fish farmer will have plenty of stock to grow on.

Naturally, the number of larvae in the water column depends on the number of spawning adults in the area. The second stage of aquaculture is that in which the aquaculturist gathers together many adults either in a natural body of water or in artificial ponds or tanks. His objective here is to ensure that there is a large number of spawners lying close together in order to ensure a large supply of larvae from which to harvest his spat. This is called semi-extensive aquaculture and we will see an example of it when we discuss the cultivation of the flat oyster.

Aquaculture will only be successful if the operator understands the needs and life cycle of the animals in his care. As scientists gather this knowledge they come to learn the exact requirements for good spawning and growth in captive individuals. When they know these, aquaculture can progress to its final mature phase in which the whole operation from adult to larva to new adult can be carried out entirely under artificial conditions. Once that is achieved the supply of spat is no longer a problem and shellfish farming becomes independent of the natural spatfall and even of the natural stocks. This is the case, for example, with cupped oysters (*Crassostrea* spp.) in many places. At this stage aquaculture may actually help nature by providing spat to be stocked out in the wild to augment a depleted natural stock, or to start a new one.

Returning now to the King scallop, Ireland had one unique scallop resource that exploded into prominence in 1979. In that year conditions in Mulroy Bay in County Donegal caused a settlement of scallop spat infinitely greater than any ever encountered before. It has been described as the biggest scallop spatfall that ever occurred in European waters. If only a fraction of one percent of the spat could be collected it would yield an abundance of scallops like never before. The spat settled fortuitously on ropes left in the water to collect mussel spat. These were not ideal collectors since scallop spat settle in the top meter or so of the water column whereas mussel ropes hang much deeper. Nevertheless, settlement on the ropes was enormous. Many spat were successfully gathered and attempts were made to grow them in lantern nets or on the sea bottom in extensive culture. More importantly, the settlement signalled that the indigenous adult spawning stock was very large and what could occur by way of spatfall in one year might also occur in others.

What has been described as "Mulroy Bay fever" now gripped the locality; thoughts of Mulroy Bay spat supplying the whole world filled the imaginings of many with visions of pockets filled with money. The adult stock was estimated at half a million individuals, enough to ensure spat supplies for years if not generations. When techniques for the successful collection of scallop spat had been developed years earlier in Japan they had lead to the emergence of a huge industry producing in excess of 500,000 tonnes of full-grown scallops a year. An Irish King scallop industry of similar magnitude seemed destined to follow. But life is rarely that simple and straightforward.

In 1980 John Slater, who had been working on scallop cultivation in Scotland, took up a post at the Institute of Technology in Letterkenny. He advised that the Scottish form of collector – small mesh nets held in a wider mesh bag suspended high in the water column – should be used in Mulroy Bay, just as he proposed to use for his own scallop enterprise. His own venture proved successful whereas those who stayed with the mussel-type collectors did not do so well. The next year all operators had changed to bag collectors and good amounts of spat were harvested. So much so, indeed, that a large amount was sold to producers in St. Brieuc in France. The "fever" was at its height and began to incite unseemly conduct between the competing participants in the fishery. In 1982 the spatfall diminished and the "fever" subsided. In the next two years no significant spat numbers were recorded and it was clear by then that something was seriously wrong.

In fact, a number of things were wrong. While spat were being harvested so too were the adults, both by dredgers and by scuba divers. That was a sure recipe for trouble. Bylaws prohibiting dredging in the North Water of Mulroy, the main centre of the stock, were quickly put in place. But unknown up until then, the spat had to cope with one of the deadliest substances ever found in the sea. Tributyl tin (TBT), a component of anti-fouling paint used widely in the 1980s to paint leisure and other watercraft, including some aquaculture structures, was identified in Mulroy Bay in 1985. So damaging to sea life is this substance that its use has been banned completely since 1989. But, has the door been bolted too late? The Mulroy stock that stood at half a million scallops in 1979 is now estimated at only 100,000 adults.

The most delicate stage of the scallop life cycle is the period immediately after settlement to a size of about ten millimetres, the "nursery" stage. Once over that stage, the small juveniles can be grown suspended in the water in nets or in plastic frames, or even scattered freely on the sea bottom in extensive culture. The only certain way to ensure that the benefit of a good spatfall can ever be translated into a large adult stock is to enhance juvenile survival through this critical nursery phase. Based on this, a strategy for an Irish scallop industry began to take shape: spat would be harvested from Mulroy, go through nursery culture in designated cultivation stations and then be delivered as juveniles to producers at various sites throughout the country. When spatfall, although variable, remained reasonable in the ensuing decade it seemed that the strategy might work. Hatcheries like Cartron Point Shellfish in County Clare where Iarlath Connellan, one of the most experienced shellfish cultivators in the country was in charge, prepared themselves as nursery stations to receive and culture the earliest spat under artificial conditions. There were plenty of good aquaculturists around Ireland waiting to receive juveniles from the nurseries for the next stage of ongrowing. The inlets of the north shore of Galway Bay, for example, where Taighde Mara had all the appropriate equipment and infrastructure in place, had still not recovered from the scallop mortalities of the cold winter of 1962/3 and were ripe for restocking.

Unfortunately, if *Pecten maximus* is the King scallop, then its offspring proved to be demanding princes and princesses. They simply did not take at all well to life in captivity. They settled well enough on the surfaces provided for them in Mulroy Bay but when removed to the nurseries they turned out to be extremely delicate. At that stage they were less than half a millimetre in size. Rearing them up to five millimetres was found to be, and is still, a very difficult task. Very few survived the early phase and to this day the growth of young scallops in captivity is a most precarious and uncertain matter. No doubt it will be mastered in due course. But the anticipated Irish scallop bonanza has not yet materialised and may not do so in the near future. A whole new industry is awaiting a breakthrough by the likes of Slater and Connellan that will catapult the scallop to the forefront of Ireland's aquaculture output. We wish them well in their important work.

Irish output of farmed scallops was only 28 tonnes in 1995 whereas the wild fisheries yielded over 400 tonnes that year. By 1999 the landings of wild King scallops were almost 1,500 tonnes (about 7.5 million individuals) and there were none from aquaculture. In contrast, King and Queen scallop spat are being successfully harvested from the wild and grown under culture in many dispersed fish farms on the west coast of Scotland. Approximately 39 tonnes of King scallops (about 200,000 individuals) and 58 tonnes of Queens (about 1.2 million individuals) were produced there in 2000, which goes to show the underdeveloped potential of Ireland's resource.

Only the muscle and the roe (the reproductive organs, called the coral or the tongue) are eaten. The muscle is pure, glistening white and the coral is two-toned. The male part of the coral is pinkish-white and the female part is orange. These bright colour differences, together with the conveniently shaped shell, mean that the gastronomy of scallops can be marvellously versatile and its presentation visually attractive. Not that they need any dressing-up. Scallop meat is so wonderfully sweet and delicious that it would grace any meal. The recipe in the accompanying box is worth trying, but be careful not to overcook the scallops!

INGREDIENTS

6 King scallops from Valentia. 4 spring onions, chopped medium. 2 cloves garlic, finely chopped. Flat-leaf Parsley, chopped roughly. Champagne, optional Cognac

METHOD

Fry the onions, garlic and some chopped ginger (optional) in butter. Open scallops and retain the liquor. Discard all the loose material retaining only the muscle and coral. Slice the muscle into two thick medallions but leave the pink and cream coral intact. Add the scallop meat and the liquor to the onion mixture in the pan and toss over a high heat for 4 minutes. Remove scallops from the pan and keep warm.
Add two glasses of champagne to the onion mixture and juices in the pan. (Optional: add one tablespoon Cognac.) Reduce over a high heat. Place the scallops in the half shell, pour over the reduced sauce and garnish with the chopped parsley.

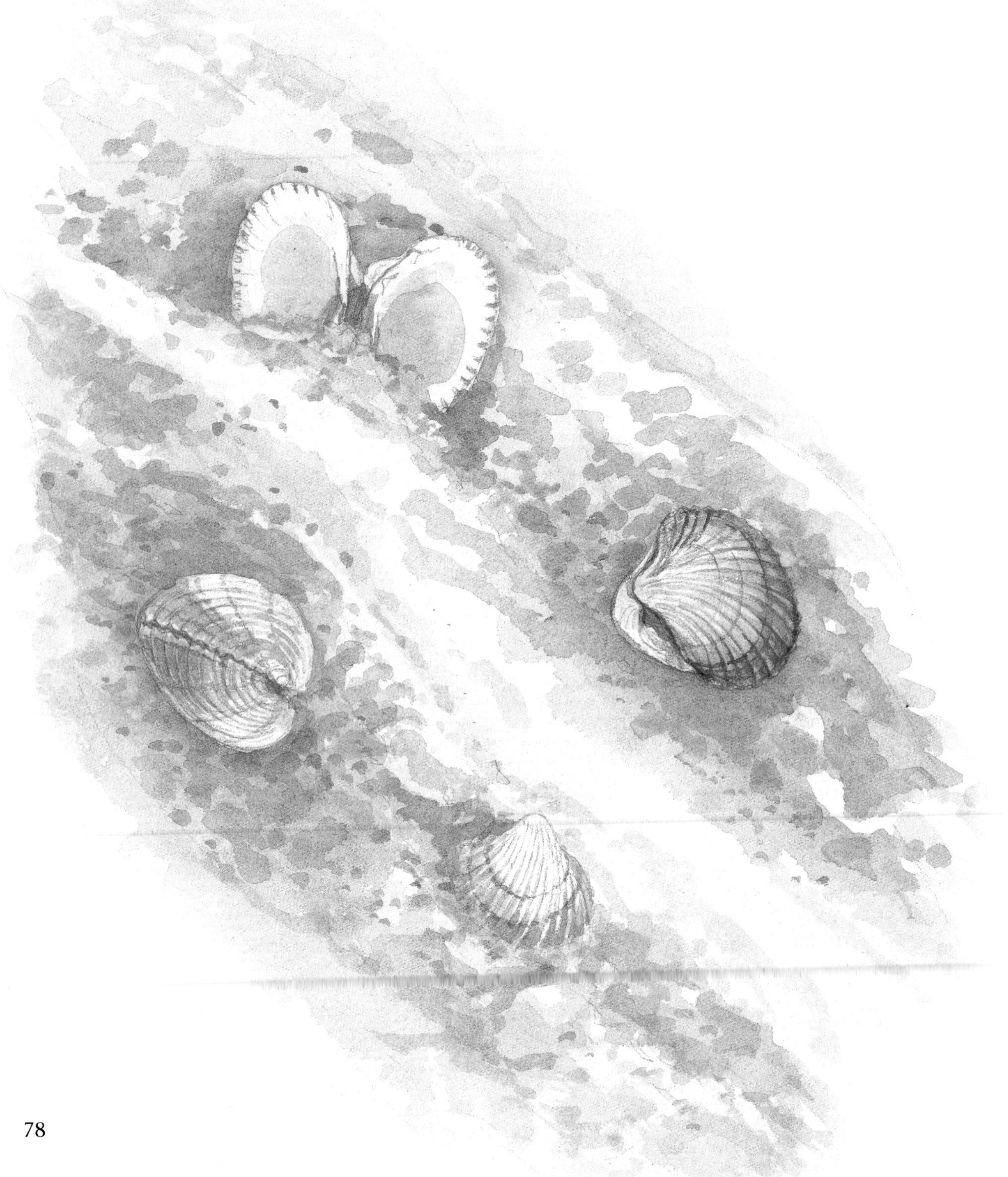

Chapter 6

COCKLES, CLAMS AND RAZORFISH

The sea here is plentifully stored with fish . . . and no less liberall of shellfish, as oysters, scallops, cokles, muscles, razures, together with lobsters, crabs, shromps etc.

R. O'Flaherty, *Iar Connaught*, 1846.

CON VONGOLE! What bliss these words conjure up all over Italy but especially around Naples and along the Adriatic coast! Spaghetti or risotto *con vongole* with tiny clams in delicious, heavenly sauce – what better *primo piatto* could one ask for? In Valencia, Spain, there are few main course dishes to beat *paella marinera* with the clams (and the mussels, too) bursting out all over, shells and all! Only the zoological purist or the Michelin inspector would have the temerity to enquire what species of clam was actually included in either dish – as if it really mattered! Zoologically, "clam" is a loose term used to describe members of a variety of different bivalve families such as the *Cardiidae* (the cockles), the *Veneridae* (the carpet shells), the *Solenidae* (the razorfish) and the *Myidae* (the family to which the American soft-shell clams belong). All clams burrow to a greater or lesser extent into sandy or muddy shores at or near low tide level. In Scotland, scallops were sometimes called clams but that is unusual.

The cockle has been a long time favourite with people all over Europe, perhaps because it was easy to collect at low tide. In Ireland, two species occur widely, the common cockle *Cerastoderma edule* and the lagoon cockle *C. glaucum,* the former being much more abundant. A number of other varieties also occur here but in much lower frequency. Cockles, called *ruachain* in Irish, look positively sturdy, almost aggressively so, compared with the other clam species. That, of course, has not in any way lessened their acceptability in the cuisines of Italy and Spain. Nor was Molly Malone reticent in crying "cockles and mussels!" on the streets of Dublin. Indeed cockles were good Dublin fare long before mussels became popular. They were abundant on the shores around the capital up until very recent times. At the beginning of the twentieth century it was estimated that seventy to eighty thousand quarts of cockles (between two and three million shells) were consumed annually in the city. At least three fourths of these were eaten raw, testament to the clean waters of Dublin Bay then, or to the strong constitutions of Dubliners then as now. In all months except those of the winter, cockle gatherers raked the strands of the southern shore of the Bay and subsequently hawked their wares in the poorer parts of the city. Three pence (about one Euro cent) a quart was the usual price so they were within the financial reach of most people. Oysters may well have been the favourite of the poor in the English cities of the industrial revolution but cockles held that role of honour in the second city of the Empire. In Belfast too, we are informed, cockles were ". . . hawked in the evenings through the working class districts, sold to the residents, and in public houses. Rag gatherers frequently carry them and exchange them to children for rags and bones." It is, perhaps, little wonder that as prosperity spread in urban Ireland cockles and mussels, and their hawkers, were relegated to nostalgic street ballads.

Cockles, sand gapers, razorfish, and scallops were collected by hand along the west and southwest coasts whenever there was a big strand. Maxwell's description of cockle gathering on Achill Island in 1832 is worth quoting: "A crowd of a more youthful description of the peasantry are collected every spring-tide to gather cockles . . . The quantities of these shellfish thus procured would almost exceed belief; and I have frequently seen more than would load a donkey collected during one tide by the children of a single cabin. They form a valuable and wholesome addition to the limited variety that the Irish peasant boasts at his humble board; and afford children, too young for other tasks, a safe and useful employment". He went on to mention other shellfish as well: "There are other shellfish greatly prized by the peasantry," he wrote, ". . . such as razorfish, clams and various kinds of mussels, which I have never had the curiosity to eat" – nor the necessity or hunger either, one imagines.

According to Tom Mitchell, whose family has a long history of cockle gathering, they were a great favourite in Ballina, Co. Mayo up until relatively modern times. There is even a small, old street in the town called "Cockle Street" and shells are very commonly unearthed whenever building foundations are opened. Collection was done in the same manner as in Maxwell's time.

The gatherers left town by donkey and cart to get to the cockle bed at Bartragh, some miles distant. There they gathered their prey using what they called a "crommel". This was an old sickle, beyond use for cutting vegetation. (*Crom* means bent or bowed in Irish.) With this in one hand they scraped the sandy bed wherever they saw the fish's burrow holes, lifting the cockles with the other hand and putting them into a small *galún*. They were then transferred into a larger bucket in the cart. When they had finished their collecting the catch was washed in a perforated bucket that was placed in a stream of seawater so that all adherent sand was washed away. Then it was back to town to sell the goods, hawking them door-to-door. Each collector had his own customers. A good day's work would yield around 20 kilos of cockles that would give a small enough return for the day's labour. The season started in late April because here, too, tradition had it that cockles needed "three drinks of seawater in April" before they were worth eating. The season went on until September.

Only adults from the town engaged in the fishery – farmers and children played no part at all. From the nineteenth century on, shellfish appear to have been favoured more by urban than by rural populations. It is not clear why this was, but maybe the shellfish trade needed a large, very localized market to be profitable, as shellfish were too perishable to be hawked widely in warm weather. Cockles are particularly susceptible to warm, dry conditions and do not last long out of water. Elsewhere in Ireland they were once widely gathered for local consumption, the main centres being Dundalk Bay, Waterford, Wexford, Kinsale, Ballycastle (Co. Mayo), Ballisodare Bay (Co. Sligo) and Strangford Lough. All of these except Ballycastle, which is near Ballina, are close to urban centres where the catch could be easily disposed of. In Ballina itself the cockle trade has ended now, Tom Mitchell (Snr.) being one of the last to have engaged in it. But one can still enjoy a bowl of "Crocket's Cockle Chowder" in Crocket's pub at The Quay in the town. The recipe is local and the cockles now come from Streedagh in Co. Sligo. With a great dollop of fresh cream on top and a "bate" of brown bread on the side, it makes a lunch fit for a king. *Bia Rí ruachan*, for sure!

Pat and Mary Power of the Cooley Peninsula in County Louth still collect cockles in the traditional way in Dundalk Bay. Near low tide they drive a tractor out over the exposed strand to the cockle bed. There, using an ordinary garden rake, they dig up the cockles. The technique involves raking the sand vigorously just below water level (Fig. 45). Raking the packed, exposed sand would be much more demanding. When the rake strikes a cockle it can easily be lifted on the tines and dropped into a bucket or *galún* (Fig. 46). Only large ones (Fig. 47) are taken, all small ones under about thirty millimetres being returned to the water. A few hours of raking yields a satisfactory catch and the gatherers return to land. On the way back the cockles are stored in bags in a small loch – a natural hollow in the sand that holds water even when the tide goes fully out. A buyer takes the cache away twice a week and the ultimate destination is the Spanish market. Both the pace and the extent of this family enterprise ensure its sustainability, but even so, plans are in train to investigate the artificial cultivation of cockles in the region. There are scattered instances of cockles still being collected in the traditional way in other places in Ireland but not in anything like the extent to which it was pursued in the past. "Cockle Point" and "Cockle Strand" are Irish placenames so common on the coast that we can well understand just how abundant and widely distributed the species once was.

Fig. 45. Raking cockles in Dundalk Bay, Co. Louth. Note how the raking is done in the shallow water, not on the exposed sand.

The sand gaper (*Mya arenaria*) is known in Irish as *an breallach* and the razorfish (*Ensis* sp.) as *an scian mhara*. In fact we have two species of gaper and four species of razorfish but all of these are not separately named in Irish. The sand gapers are known in America as the "soft shell clams" and they constitute the basic ingredient in clam chowder. Throughout the world, gapers are commercially important but in Ireland they never achieved high status, although they were gathered and eaten by the poorest people. In Carlingford Lough, sand gapers were so common within living memory that they were sold, suitably stripped of their ugly siphons, as "utility oysters" at the shellfish stalls in Omeath. They were also commonly eaten within living memory around Killala and Ballycastle in North Mayo, where there are large natural beds holding a variety of clam species.

Fig. 46. Mary Power lifts cockles on the tines of the rake and drops them into the galún. Unlike collecting winkles, it is not necessary to bend down to gather cockles, making the task much easier.

Fig. 47. What a whopper! A cockle over 50 millimetres is a fine catch. Small cockles are returned to the water as a conservation measure.

Men, women and children took a hand at clam gathering, which required some skill and agility. When the strand is exposed some species lie close to the surface or protrude slightly from it. On the occurrence of any activity they burrow deeper with great rapidity. Even digging with a spade or shovel, the usual method of fishing them, they can be hard to catch, so deeply do some species descend into the substrate when pursued. Nevertheless, experienced people could gather a good *cléibhín*-full during low tide and enjoy a decent feed for their efforts.

Tradition has it that if one whistled musically clams stopped their descent and could be easily captured. But I suspect that this advice was simply a ruse to make fun of anyone gullible enough to try it. In Irish, *breallán,* the generic word for clam, also means a fool or a mug, which would confirm this suspicion. Alternatively, gatherers tell us that cockles make a whistling sound when out of water so maybe the belief grew that whistling would attract other cockles? Terns and gulls take their chance at catching clams, too, but with much greater success than humans.

Another means of collecting clams, especially gapers and razorfish, should be mentioned and that is by pouring granular salt on them, or more accurately, on the mouth of the keyhole-shaped holes which mark where they burrow. They rise up in the sand when they sense the salt and can then be grabbed if one is quick enough. Scientists have used the method in recent years to collect samples for biological research so it certainly is effective, strange as it may seem. Salt was never that easily come by in Ireland long ago so I suspect the salting technique is not as old here as it may be in Britain. The late Dr. Arthur Went described a traditional

Irish method of collection that involved inserting a spear into the animal's burrow. The razorfish reputedly closed its valves on the spear tip when touched and was then drawn out of the hole when the spear was raised. G. H. Lewes, writing in 1860, described a somewhat similar and probably more effective implement used in Britain. An iron rod with a barb at its end "like a harpoon" was inserted into the burrow. When the clam was encountered the rod was given a half turn that caused the barb to fix in the flesh or in the shell. The animal was then drawn up. A useful implement could be made easily and cheaply from the rib of an umbrella, sharpened and given a barb at the tip.

All of these methods were slow and not very efficient. The implement used inevitably damaged the clam so that it soon died and had to be eaten right away. Traditional fishers were therefore unlikely to deplete a clam bed very easily. Newer, mechanised gathering methods have no such saving grace. In 1997 a huge new razorfish bed about 21 square kilometres in extent was discovered in the Irish Sea off the coast of Co. Meath at Gormanstown. Within two years fishermen had harvested over 1,000 tonnes of the razorfish species *Ensis siliqua* by hydraulic (fluidised bed) dredging, a ruthlessly effective technique, and the new bed became utterly exhausted. Attention then turned to the coasts of Mayo and Galway where the most abundant razorfish species is *Ensis arcuata*. The western beds are more localised and less extensive and, once their precise locations are known, they are less likely to survive concentrated attack.

There are very many species of Venerid clams – not even the experts are agreed as to exactly how many distinct species exist in Ireland – and the most desirable of them all is the one called the native carpet clam, *Tapes decussata*. In order to distinguish it from other venerid clams, the carpet clam is given the specific Irish name *an cairpéad*, an inelegant, politically correct transliteration that does nothing for the clam and even less for the language. In Bantry Bay it was known vernacularly as *an chircín* (a diminutive of the word *cearc*, it means a bantam hen) or as *an chearc gheal*, the bright hen. This is rather interesting since in Devon it was known as the "pullet" because the colour and patterning of some individuals were suggestive of the plumage of a speckled hen (Fig. 48). Elsewhere in the south of England it was called the "hen cockle". In Clew Bay it is called the "ladyfish" and in Donegal the "lady cockle". The French call it by the attractive name *palourde*. Whatever we call it (my own choice is *an chircín*), all of

Fig. 48. Young palourdes or carpet clams are coloured and speckled rather like a young hen!

Fig. 49. "There's one!" Palourdes are gathered by digging near low water when the tide has gone out. A pointed shovel is the best implement for the task and John Kelly of Kenmare the best person to wield it!

these names conjure up a more feminine image for the species that contrasts with the more masculine image of the clumpier, sturdier and less delicate common cockle. It is a shallow burrower in sandy or muddy substrates near low water mark and it is found in many southern European countries where it was fished traditionally by digging, raking or dredging.

The fishing method traditionally used in Ireland was to dig with a pointed shovel (Fig. 49). In Kenmare Bay and elsewhere in south Kerry, John Kelly is the undisputed champion clam digger. As one local put it ". . . he would win the 'All Ireland' for clam digging!" In Kerry and many other places, an "All Ireland" title in any endeavour would be a most coveted and respected distinction. John is unlikely ever to be ousted from his supremacy: there are few enough clam diggers left and the palourde itself is much less common in the wild than previously. Its present relative scarcity may, paradoxically, save it from complete extinction.

The over-exploitation suffered by the razorfish on the east coast in recent times mirrored what had occurred earlier with the palourde in the west. One of the experts of the time described the event as the "clam boom of 1974 to 1976". Up to 1972 total Irish landings of palourdes never exceeded 10 tonnes a year. This rose to 15 tonnes in 1973, 19 in 1974 and 117 tonnes in 1975. From August 1974 the price paid by the dealers doubled from £0.63 to £1.26 per kg. (Today, wild palourdes fetch about six euro a kilogram at first sale, a five-fold increase). Hundreds of gatherers descended on the natural beds in Galway Bay to share in the bonanza. The rich bed at Rusheen Bay in the Galway suburb of Salthill was completely wiped out by only 30 gatherers in just five months. Further away, along the shore adjoining the famous Clarinbridge oyster beds, crowds estimated at upwards of 300 persons gathered an estimated 13 kg each in April of 1976, ravaging not only the palourde bed but also damaging the oyster beds nearby.

Similar occurrences were reported from elsewhere in Ireland. In some places, tractors and ploughs were used to turn over the beds, with children following behind to gather up the exposed clams in the same manner as potatoes used to be harvested. By the end of 1976 the short-lived clam boom was over. Beds that at the beginning held stocks of more than one kilogram per square meter were left totally depleted and the stocks have never fully recovered.

Such over-fishing is neither unique to shellfish nor unique to Ireland. Learning to manage natural resources in a sustainable way is the severe test that now faces us in many human activities and our success or otherwise in this will determine whether native species like the palourde can last into the future. Sometimes what we do with one species has direct consequences for another. This is particularly true with clams. Where one species is found many others occur also, so that harvesting techniques may collect many different species as an inadvertent by-catch to the main target species. Normally the by-catch species are in lower abundance and can ill afford to be exploited in this way. The "fluidised bed" dredging technique, which scours and suspends the bottom sediment by blasting it with water before gathering all the dislodged, surface-living and burrowing organisms into the dredge box is a most indiscriminate and devastating harvesting method (Fig 50). Once aboard the dredger, no shellfish of any species are ever thrown back alive, and many other invertebrate species are killed too. If we visit any fish market in Europe, or take a stroll among the restaurants in Petite rue des Bouchers in Brussels, we cannot but be amazed at the sheer variety of shellfish on offer. Many of these are gathered opportunistically and some are species under threat of extinction because of their small standing population sizes, low recruitment levels or slow replacement rates. It is for this reason that our approach to native stocks needs to be sensible, based on best practice and one that wins the consent of all the resource users. That is why we are now championing the CLAMS approach outlined in chapter 10.

Fig. 50. A "fluidised bed" dredge. A hose from the boat is attached to the spout on the left and water is forced out under pressure through the three nozzles directed towards the sea bottom in front of the dredge box. This causes the sediment and all the animals in it to become suspended in the water. The dredge is pulled forward so that everything in suspension is pushed into the dredge box. Sand washes out of the box but all the animals are retained inside whether or not they are the specific target of the dredger.

For diversity of shellfish stocks and for aquaculture, Ireland had its own historical "centre of excellence" in the nineteenth century. County Sligo – its name in Irish, *Sligeach*, means a shelly place – boasted an abundance and diversity of shellfish unsurpassed at other Irish sites. Its oysters were famous, its cockles abundant, its clams diverse and its mussels abounding. Salmon thrived in its main river, the Garavogue. Because salmon could not enter the other Sligo river, the Ballisodare River, Edward Joshua Cooper constructed the first fish ladder in Ireland in the 1830s causing a new salmon stock to occupy the river, long before anyone else thought that was feasible. In nearby Tanrego Demesne the only Irish oyster culture enterprise modelled on the French *parc* system operated during the 1870s. Around Sligo Bay, more than 22 million American (*Crassostrea virginica*), Portuguese (*Crassostrea angulata*) and European (*Ostrea edulis*) oysters from Holland, from Auray in Brittany and from Arcachon were laid down on the local shellfish beds between 1870 and 1890. Sadly, all the oysters and their cultivators had gone from Sligo by the start of the twentieth century. The cockles, the mussels and the clams went later (many by steamer to markets in Liverpool and Manchester) and Sligo's place of honour in the shellfish story passed to other Irish localities. But the place that had produced great aquaculture entrepreneurs once could do so again, as it was to do in the 1980s.

By 1980 it was clear from the devastation wreaked by the "clam boom" that Irish stocks of the palourde would never be capable of sustaining the demands being made on them. All over Europe too, stocks were in decline even as demand continued to rise. In France the shortfall in clams was met by the importation and eventual artificial cultivation of a related but much hardier species, the Manila clam, *Ruditapes philippinarum*. This species has a much greater tolerance of salinity and temperature fluctuations and is altogether easier to grow. Aware of its potential, the Shellfish Research Laboratory at Carna, Co. Galway imported the species into Ireland (from Conwy Shellfish Experimental Station in Wales) with full quarantine precautions in 1982. The imports were induced to spawn in the Carna laboratory and independent trials made on the offspring by Taighde Mara and the Carna Laboratory confirmed their suitability to Irish conditions. At various sites throughout the country they grew faster with better overall survival than the native clams then being tested in culture. With the culture technique largely mastered, what was needed was someone to take the new species on to commercial production. Such "scaling up" is not always easy or successful: what may work under laboratory conditions does not always transfer to commercial scale and the persons who attempt the task of commercialisation are real pioneers in their field.

Charles Kelly, a Sligo entrepreneur, was one to take up the challenge. He and the late Dr. Tim Smith, an experienced shellfish biologist who had trained in Carna, set up Sligo Aquaculture, Ireland's first-ever commercial clam enterprise and set about finding a site suitable for their cultivation plans. The then owners and the heir to the Lissadell Estate at Drumcliffe Bay were delighted to offer space on the Estate's foreshore to the new enterprise. Josslyn Gore-Booth was eager to see the Estate, at that time somewhat in distress, participate in a new resource-based activity, if only to help with the upkeep of the property. Kevin O'Kelly of Taighde Mara had already shown that the site was an excellent one for Manila clam growth. In fact the location was the site of Sir Robert Gore-Booth's chartered oyster bed where he had laid down half a million American, French and Dutch oysters exactly one hundred years previously and that had been quite a successful venture in the first flush of oyster culture in Sligo. On a darker note, when Sir Robert had received no satisfaction by writing to Sir Robert Peel in 1865 about poaching on the bed, he took to shooting at the fishermen in Drumcliffe Bay in hopes to dissuade them from poaching his oysters! According to the Fishery Inspector at the time, this caused Sligo to become "the scene of frequent riot and disturbance, threatening the loss of life" and the local Resident Magistrate took serious fright: "I fear there will be bloodshed amongst the parties unless I obtain a general authority to use the Coast Guards," he wrote. Thankfully, the courts settled the matter without bloodshed or Coast Guards when the jury acquitted the fishermen of any wrongdoing. But they were left in no doubt about the ownership of the oyster bed. It is important to realise that the public has the common law right to take any living fish or shellfish from the sea unless the fish are in beds or in structures for which clear, unambiguous and uncontested ancient title or modern licence exists. The chartered status of the Lissadell bed (it is held under a grant of ownership of very ancient provenance) made it safe in modern times from possible vexatious claims of public interest and the need for a special aquaculture licence.

Undaunted by its inauspicious history, Kelly and Smith laid down their first stock of Manila clams on the Lissadell bed in 1984. Fortune favoured the brave, at least enough to encourage them to construct a hatchery in the Estate's stable yard within firing range of Lissadell House. Kevin O'Kelly (Fig. 51) then joined the venture as clam hatchery manager and Ireland's first commercial clam farm was really up and running – this time with the support of the Gore-Booth family and without the tiniest whiff of gunsmoke! It was not just the shellfishery and the family's attitude to it that underwent dramatic change in the period between Sir Robert and Josslyn. The House and family participated in the important literary and historical events that marked the early years of the twentieth century in Ireland, through the activities of Eva and Constance (Markievicz) Gore-Booth.

Cultivating the Manila clam is both easy and difficult. Adults can be easily induced to mature and spawn in captivity, provided they are kept well fed and warm. At spawning, the females produce large numbers of eggs that they release into the water column in the breeding tanks. This stimulates the males to release great clouds of sperm and the eggs are soon fertilized. The free-swimming larvae are then cultured at high density in the tanks and this is where the difficulty starts. Larvae require copious supplies of suitable algal food that has to be supplied alive and fresh. Shellfish hatcheries are as much producers of massive volumes of algae as they are producers of shellfish. The algae are grown in very large plastic bags, using a suitable starter culture, sunlight, heat, fertilizer and filtered seawater. Getting the algal production right is a main determinant of the success of shellfish culture. About six kilograms of algae are needed to produce one kilogram of shellfish so the scale and the cost of the operation can be significant. When the food is correct the larvae grow well and they metamorphose into spat after about 20 days. The spat settle on the sides and bottom of the tank from where they can be collected for further rearing in other receptacles.

At this stage they are tiny, shelled creatures and very delicate. They must be reared in the hatchery until they are about 3 to 4 millimetres in size at which stage they can be moved out to the sea. The slower they grow the longer they must stay in the hatchery and the greater the cost of production. Laid out on special trays, made of timber frames with a fine mesh floor, or made entirely of perforated plastic, they are put out on the seashore for their first year of life. The trays are held off the bottom in stacks or on trestles or wheels (Fig. 52), so that the clams are safe

Fig. 51. Kevin O'Kelly farms clams on the Lissadell oyster bed at Drumcliffe in Sligo Bay. The horizontal ridges in the sand in the foreground are rows of palourdes covered with protective mesh. Benbulben is the dramatic mountain escarpment profiled in the background.

from crabs and from the smothering effect of shifting sand and mud. This is sometimes called the nursery stage of culture. They are brought ashore periodically for grading so that the fastest growers, those about 15 to 20 millimetres in size, can be taken on quickly to the final growth stage. For final growth, the small clams are seeded at about 300 per square meter on the seabed in long rows. The clams burrow in to a depth of 8 to 10 centimetres. The rows are then completely covered with a plastic mesh that is carefully buried all along the sides of the rows so that crabs cannot penetrate into the clams by burrowing under the net. Oystercatchers, too, are serious predators of young clams so the net cover must be sufficiently strong to exclude them and their probing beaks. The rows look like "lazy beds" (the traditional West of Ireland way of growing potatoes in ridges separated by furrows) in the sea (Fig. 53). It takes about two more seasons of growth before the clams are ready for market at 20 grams weight or greater. They are then harvested mechanically using a clam harvester developed at Lissadell. The commercial success of the operation is determined largely by the exclusion of predators and by the success of the clams in surviving the huge mortalities that normally occur after their first winter of life. In other words, the culture technique is easy but difficult at the same time and there is still plenty to be investigated before we can say that artificial clam culture is really fully mastered in Ireland.

Because of the difficulty in reliably producing adequate quantities of clam spat at home, some shellfish farmers import spat from abroad to make up their stock. This is a decidedly risky strategy – when you buy from abroad you may bring in

Fig. 52. Trays for holding young clams are mounted on wheels and joined together in long trains that can be pulled out onto the clam bed by tractor. They remain on the bed until the young clams have grown sufficiently to be safely buried in clam rows.

Fig. 53. Half-grown clams are buried in long rows that are then covered with mesh to keep crabs and other predators away. The long rows look rather like shallow "lazy beds", the traditional way that potatoes were planted in the west of Ireland. The dark rows are the ridges containing the clams.

more than you bargained for and the inadvertent introduction of unwanted organisms, especially pathogens and parasites, is something that is unlikely to benefit anyone. The virus causing Brown Ring Disease (BRD) in clams is believed to have been introduced into Ireland in this way. It is the single most serious threat to the potential development of Irish clam farming, and ensuring that it is not spread any further is the major task facing the industry today.

The palourde is just one of the many kinds of Venerid clams we have in Ireland. When the other species are collected – usually as a by-catch – they are not normally distinguished by an Irish name, although each does have its own Latin name and distinct identity. Names like *Venus verrucosa, Venerupis aurea, Tapes rhomboides* and *Dosinia exoleta* all mean something particular to the zoologist and they represent important elements of our native molluscan fauna. But they ring no bells with the public at large. One certainly meets with them in the cuisine and on the restaurant tables of Europe and it is hard to imagine some famous dishes without them.

Another Venerid species – the quahog, *Mercenaria mercenaria* – is not native to Ireland but is worthy of mention. It was supposedly introduced accidentally to Southampton Water in England when live clams were thrown overboard from an American liner. However, it was also introduced at other earlier times,

Fig. 54. An ordinary box dredge. Note the absence of the nozzles shown in the "fluidised bed" box dredge in figure 50.

especially when the importation of American oysters was at its height at the end of the nineteenth century. In any case, the Southampton *arriviste* adapted well to local conditions and a self-sustaining population became established. The Conwy Shellfish Laboratory gathered some of them and commenced to cultivate them artificially during the 1960s. Subsequently, suitable disease-free hatchery stock became available from Conwy and the Department of Agriculture and Fisheries imported a consignment for growth trials in 1969. These were very early days in modern Irish aquaculture and the Department was not at all certain that shellfish farming was a suitable road to be taken by this country. Further imports were made in 1970 and 1971 and preliminary growth experiments were carried out in Wexford Harbour, Bannow Bay, Cork Harbour, Oysterhaven and Clew Bay. Results were not at all bad for the layings in Wexford and Cork. But the Department seemed to lose either faith or hope in the experiment and the exercise was abandoned even as the cultivation of other species was getting underway here. Today, there is no culturing of quahogs in Ireland although suitable spat is widely available from hatcheries in North America and elsewhere. It certainly warrants another chance under Irish conditions.

There are, of course, other species of clams that are not Venerids such as the peppery furrow shell, *Scrobicularia* (traditionally eaten in Britain), the Thin Tellin, *Tellina tenuis* said to have been eaten by the people of the Galway coast in the nineteenth century and the surf clam *Spisula solida*. This last species is common in sub-tidal shelly sand but its distribution tends to be patchy and local populations may be small. In recent years fisheries using ordinary box dredges (Fig. 54) and hydraulic "fluidised bed" dredges (Fig. 50) have started on the south coast. Landings up to 500 tonnes per year have been made in recent years but there is reason to believe that such catches may be unsustainable. We have already seen that the hydraulic dredge is a most indiscriminate engine of capture. Can we really afford to continue using it on our precious and threatened stocks?

Fig. 55. "What beauties!" European flat oysters. This species is native to Ireland but unfortunately wild stocks are now severely depleted in many places. Photo: Marianne Whilde.

Chapter 7 THE EUROPEAN FLAT OYSTER

"The oyster is said to want nothing that it should have and to have nothing that it should want."

J. Philpots, *The Oyster,* 1891.

How can anyone ever again praise the flat oyster adequately now that Heaney has spoken:

Our shells clacked on the plates,
My tongue was a filling estuary,
My palate hung with starlight:
As I tasted the salty Pleiades
Orion dipped his foot in the water.

Seamus Heaney, *Oysters.*

All the subtlety, all the magic and the classical allusion captured in these words pay fitting homage to the native European flat oyster. Two thousand years ago the Caesars loved them, shipping them all the way from Britain to Rome to adorn their tables, enhance their feasts and engorge their guests. The numbers they ate were truly enormous, beyond the most craven glutton's wildest dreams. Such indulgence – Heaney's *"glut of privilege"* – had its cost of course, and even as oysters attained a reputation for coming up as easily as they went down, the Empire itself tottered and fell. Fit for Emperors and Kings, flat oysters became the food of the poor in the nineteenth century and now once again, as they become scarcer and scarcer, they recede almost out of the reach of all but the well to do:

See that bivalve social climber
Feeding the rich Mrs. Hoggenheimer,
Think of his joy as he gaily glides
Down the middle of her gilded insides.
Proud little oyster!

(Cole Porter, *The Tale of the Oyster*).

But the memory of them lingers on for the rest of us and, thankfully, they have not yet entirely disappeared from Ireland. One is almost reluctant to admit this – it is natural to keep the places where precious things are to be had a secret to oneself. But really, there are no secrets of any kind in Ireland – we just pretend not to know, otherwise what could we possibly talk about? So the Irish places for wild oysters are well known. Tralee Bay, Galway Bay, Achill and Loughs Swilly and Foyle are the last remaining places of the wild, native flat oyster *Ostrea edulis* (in Irish *an t-oisre*) in Ireland. They can be bought and eaten all over the country, but all wild flat oysters come from one of these sources (Fig 55).

That is not the way it always was. At one time almost every bay and many offshore banks had natural beds of oysters, so abundantly stocked by nature that they were thought to be inexhaustible. Eager as always to profit from even the most fundamental human needs, the "powers that be", both ecclesiastical and civil, exploited this rich resource by tithes, taxes, legislation and usurpation. The priory of St. Catherine's in Waterford, for example, held the tithes of oysters gathered from far-away Ringaskiddy in Cork Harbour and the monastery of Scattery Island in the Shannon Estuary had a tithe of one thousand oysters from every boat-load going into Limerick. On the civil side, too, the taxman raised his head early on. The first recorded taxation of oysters is a report of the payment to the Revenue Receiver of Old Ross of six shillings and eight pence by Philip Bentee in 1281 for oyster beds ("*pro terras ostredan*") in Wexford Harbour. In Dublin, the customs of the fish market in the fourteenth century included a toll ". . . of every boatload of oysters, if sold at the stalls one penny, if sold at the boat, nil". A number of landowners even put a charge on the boats dredging opposite their lands although this was contrary to common law. For instance, the Marquis of Anglesey levied an annual charge of five shillings on each boat dredging the public oyster bed in Carlingford Lough at a time when there were over 400 boats so engaged – yielding a tidy enough income from an illegitimate charge. Since the fishermen were his tenants at will there was little chance that they would object to that blatant extortion.

Freemen of Dublin City had the right to dredge oysters freely within the Bar, that is in the inner bay, where the main oyster bed was at Poolbeg. In 1595 the Corporation ordered that they restore to the bed all the gravel and stones brought up by the dredges ". . . for the better preserving of the Pool". In this way the Corporation was endeavouring to ensure the sustainability of the oyster resource long before that idea became politically correct. By 1700 the Corporation had put the beds out to lease at a yearly rent of five pounds and with the added, valuable condition that the lessee "... within twelve months replenish the beds with a sufficient quantity of oysters from Arklow and Glasgurrig [near Cahore Point in Co. Wexford] and to leave the bed well stocked upon the expiration of the lease". From then on, all the Dublin beds, within and without the bar, were stocked with oysters from Arklow and elsewhere, thus guaranteeing a supply of oysters for the capital city where they were greatly esteemed. The very fact that it was necessary to bring in oysters from elsewhere indicates that even then the local resource was in serious decline. But the same was true of the beds near the other Irish coastal towns also. Most of the accessible stocks were under threat from over-exploitation long before the oyster boom of the nineteenth century.

So popular were oysters that many towns had ordinances protecting their local supply from outsiders. In Youghal, the Corporation went as far as to introduce rationing! In 1734 the Corporation agreed with its lessee Nichol Giles a fixed price of 16 pence per hundred oysters (a good deal for him at the time) on the condition "... that he be obliged to supply the Town with the same and not sell more than half a hundred to one person at once, until oysters are more plenty". By 1755 no oysters could be carried outside the town for sale until the town itself was well supplied. The fixed price had risen to two shillings a hundred by 1761 and the new lessee had to guarantee to provide 40,000 oysters to Youghal in the first three years of his lease.

Somewhat similar ordinances were in operation in Kinsale in 1712. The Corporation there ordained that "... no western oysters be sold by huxters until they have been cried about the town and offered to public sale at the key four days, the price to be as the Sovereign shall direct and that notice be given by the bell". (The "Sovereign" of Kinsale was an office established by King Edward VII in 1334; the holder was a kind of mayor of the town and admiral of the port.) The problem was that the great demand in Cork was drawing the oysters away and Kinsale Corporation was having none of that. It was decreed, "... no joulter [shall] presume to carry any oysters dredged in this harbour to Cork or elsewhere before the town is first served".

From Kinsale along the south coast and up the west coast, urban centres were less developed than elsewhere and the oyster beds survived a little longer in these areas. The beds in almost all the western bays and inlets were still producing oysters right up to the Great Famine and later. Dredging and hand picking at low tide were carried out in many places but because of the remoteness of the areas involved, prices were low and trade was small. Prices of four or five pence per long hundred (ten dozen or 120 oysters) were not uncommon in the 1830s when oysters were sold by the cartload. Consumption was local or, in those towns with a sea connection to Britain like Sligo, the oysters were shipped out by steamer to Liverpool later in the century.

By far the most developed trade was that from the Mayo beds, extending from Clew Bay to Belmullet. One contemporary commentator gave the following description of the Clew Bay oyster trade in 1835 when upwards of 50 boats and over 200 men were engaged in the fishery: ". . . Oysters retail at 3 to 6 pence per 120 but are sold at less than half this rate to carriers who take them through the country, and sometimes to Dublin, retailing them in the towns on the route: the largest portion is taken to the County Clare. Dredging is practiced at all times of the year and when the oysters cease to be in season large quantities of them are sent to the Clare beds". The Clare beds were the famous Pouldoddy, Burrin and Red Bank beds situated between Kinvara and Bell Harbour on the southern shore of Galway Bay. These had supplied the needs of Dublin for many years prior to the nineteenth century and their native stocks had therefore become depleted very early. Thereafter they were replenished with Mayo and Connemara oysters that were laid down to grow and fatten prior to shipment to Dublin. Galway itself received most of its supply from the Clarinbridge beds. The dignitaries of the town could also get oysters from the local bed known as the Mayor's Bank, situated just outside the harbour. Today, Galwegians who are in the know enjoy their Galway flat oysters plump without pomp and fresh without fuss in Cyril Conlon's seafood restaurant in Eglinton Street. (When Galway flat oysters are out of season, Galway wild salmon are in season; try some at Conlon's, fresh from the salmon weir, for a real Galway treat). So, whatever about huxters, hawkers, joulters, jarveys, cadgers, criers, carriers, mongers, dealers, gougers, forestallers and other assorted persons mentioned in various oyster reports, the copious supplies of oysters that were needed and consumed in the larger Irish towns well before the nineteenth century leave no doubt that we have enjoyed a long and enthusiastic penchant for them.

Why oysters were so popular from the very earliest times has never been satisfactorily explained. Most commentators attribute to them great virtues in restoring and maintaining health. They "nourish your heart, cherish your blood" according to one Dublin ditty and an English writer once stated that they ". . . can make the sick well, render the healthy stouter, prolong the shortening days of senility and impart an additional charm to youth and beauty". These are truly great virtues that must be balanced against any vice they are thought to bring in their train. I refer, naturally, to their reputed aphrodisiacal qualities, which are said to exceed those of all other elixers, potions and concoctions.

In an account of Donegal in 1753 we read ". . . for scallops and oysters, when the tide was out, the young women waded into the sea, some of them naked, and by armfuls brought them ashore". It has become commonplace to hear the massive increase in the Irish population of the eighteenth and the early nineteenth centuries attributed solely to the consumption of potatoes. Exuberant sexual activity must also have had something to do with it and naked young women bearing armfuls of fresh oysters must have worked wonders for the manhood of Donegal! Of course the reputation of oysters as aphrodisiacs has long been celebrated and may explain some of their popularity. Even the Galway oysterman who complained that he ". . . ate a dozen on his wedding day and only six worked" could only concoct the limp excuse that they could not possibly have been "true Galway Bay oysters". The latter, he said, ". . . had never failed him!" Complicated scientific analyses have failed to show that oysters contain anything beyond protein-enriched seawater, which only explains why the Roman philosopher Seneca could write that they ". . . excite instead of satisfying the appetite, never causing indisposition, not even when eaten to excess". Science therefore has no simple explanation for their marvellous power. And why should we expect a scientific explanation anyway? Why should the oyster's magic be dispelled by the dry application of empirical evidence and logic? Is life so very long or so excessively passionate that we would wish to explode rather than enjoy one of its joyful mysteries? In this matter is it not better to travel than to arrive? And what a life-long pleasure our research travels on this topic can give us if we wield a sharp oyster knife and keep an open mind and a generous heart:

See him on his silver platter,
Watching the queens of fashion chatter.
Hearing the wives of millionaires
Discuss their marriages and their love affairs.
Thrilled little oyster!

Cole Porter, *The Tale of the Oyster.*

Sometimes we fail to appreciate the staggering numbers of oysters that were consumed in England and France once oyster eating became fashionable for city dwellers. They were the first real "fast food" for the masses of the industrial revolution. It has been estimated that one and a half thousand million oysters were consumed each year in England in the 1860s. To meet a tiny part of this demand, between ten and thirty million adult oysters were landed each year from the Irish Sea beds off Arklow and taken to an oyster depot in Beaumaris in North Wales. From there they were finally transported to the markets of Liverpool and Manchester. Because of this, Arklow experienced great prosperity at the time. Things were even more hectic in France: oyster landings from just one locality, the Bay of Cancale, exceeded 400 million each year from 1840 to 1860. Can we possibly be surprised that the natural beds would prove unable to withstand such exploitation indefinitely? First the main French and English beds were depleted. The fishermen then came to Arklow to replenish their stocks with Irish Sea oysters. When that stock began to run out the boats went further afield to the west coast of Ireland for supplies. Their arrival there represented a bonanza, however short-lived, for the impoverished population of the Achill area. "A ship which can carry 100 to 120 tons of oysters comes into the bay" wrote one person to the Fishery Commissioners in 1867 and "by some electrical means all the population who have boats are aware of it in two hours, and there are, or were, 100 dredging boats on the spot next day, all work on land being suspended until she had her cargo". Just like at Arklow, the local seed oysters were being taken away wholesale and the ultimate outcome – the demise of the local stocks – was predictable.

Traditionally, oysters were gathered from shallow water by hand or, more commonly and legally, by dredging. Originally oyster dredging was carried out by the method known as kedging, called "scoping" in Galway Bay. A small boat was rowed out onto the bed and an anchor was dropped over the bow. The boat then drifted or was rowed down-tide until all the anchor rope was paid out, that is until it reached the end of its scope. The expression for this in Galway Bay was "to cúl away" or "to cúl back" from the anchor. (*Cúl* is the Irish for "back"; as the boat moved back from the anchor it moved stern-first, a true backing process). The dredge was then shot over the stern and the boat was pulled back up-tide by hauling on the anchor rope. This dragged the dredge along the bottom behind the boat. Setting the dredge correctly was a skilled operation and on it depended the success of the fishing. The dredge was shipped every now and again and the oysters, if there were any, were sorted and kept (Fig 56). The dredge was then shot again. When the boat arrived close to the anchor point the dredge was shipped and the boat was allowed to cúl back on a slightly different track. Scoping continued in this way until nightfall or until circumstances made it advisable to come ashore. When outboard motors were introduced about forty years ago it made dredging much easier with a consequent increase in fishing intensity. Dredging today with engines and powered winches is a far cry from the relatively haphazard activity that the early efforts represented.

Fig. 56. Shipping the dredge in the time when kedging was the mode of fishing. The dredge was periodically drawn up onto the platform in the stern quarter of the boat and its contents were turned out. The oysters were kept and the debris thrown back into the sea. The man in the bow was the one who hauled on the anchor rope. Note the absence of any motor. Photo: Eric Edwards.

Since the start of the twentieth century only oysters above three inches in diameter could be legally landed so the men carried a ring with them for gauging the size of the oysters (Fig 57). When they caught small ones they did not land them immediately but deposited them in subtidal enclosures called *brácaí,* small storage areas marked off by a circle of stones that each man laid out for himself. These were generally respected on all sides, although disputes regarding exact locations and a little pilfering were not entirely unknown at a time when marker buoys were uncommon.

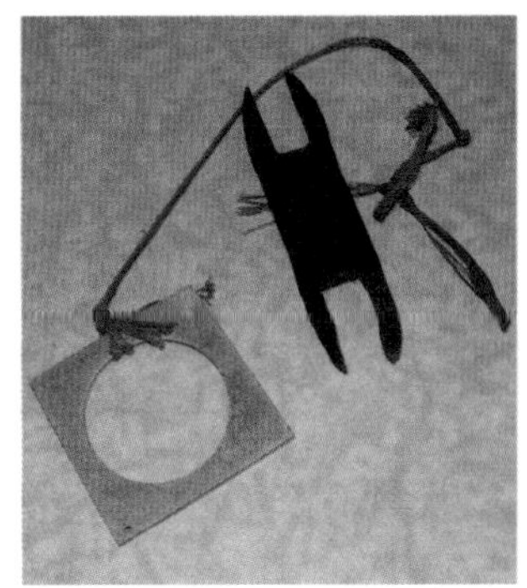

Fig. 57. A metal ring for measuring the size of oysters and a wooden needle used to make the bag of an oyster dredge in Galway Bay. Any oyster that could pass through the 76mm ring was too small to be landed legally. These items were common in the past but are now quite rare.

In 1845 the government tried to improve the ailing oyster resource by passing legislation permitting the formation of private oyster beds. The law unfortunately was ill thought out and poorly drafted, causing nearly as many new problems as it had set out to rectify. Landowners took out licences for beds contiguous to their properties and in doing so they often usurped the common law rights of the public who traditionally fished those areas. Giving landowners exclusive rights over the sea contiguous to their own property was an outrageous infringement of the rights of the public going back to Magna Charta. Nevertheless, licensed oyster farms of varying kinds sprang up at sites around the coast some of which proved quite successful at least for a time.

At Coss strand in the Kenmare River estuary the oyster ponds erected by the Mahony family of Dromore Castle around 1872 can still be seen in weedy outline when the tide is low (Fig 58), ghostly reminders of a time when nothing seemed impossible for the native oyster cultivation industry. Unfortunately a Government Oyster Commission reporting in 1870 dealt a devastating blow to that incipient industry. "We deem it incumbent on us" the Commissioners wrote, "to recommend the utmost caution with respect to all attempts at artificial cultivation, particularly as regards propagation" and they went on, understandably, to recommend only the established procedure of gathering natural oyster spat to be grown and fattened in ponds. They seemed to ignore entirely that it was a real shortage of natural spat that made artificial propagation advisable in the first instance. Whatever about the private beds, which did continue for a time and were indeed very numerous in areas like Sligo Bay, the legislation failed to stop the indiscriminate plunder of the public beds from which small oysters continued to be dredged (often for the purpose of stocking the private beds, a sure case of robbing Peter to pay Paul), so that the native stocks continued in almost terminal decline. By the end of the century the best licensed beds were reduced to growing and fattening imported oysters – many of them the cupped oyster species from Portugal and America – and not the native flat oyster. All of them had ceased operation by the start of the twentieth century. The result was that the Government established the short-lived Ardfry Experimental Oyster Cultivation Station in 1903 to address the problems of the oyster industry.

Fig. 58. The rectangular shape of one of the oyster tanks erected in the estuary of the Kenmare River, Co. Kerry around 1872 by the Mahony family is visible in weedy outline at low tide, a ghostly reminder of times past.

While in one sense this period marked the beginning of the end for native Irish flat oysters it also marked the end of the beginning of modern oyster culture, which would only come to full fruition later on in our own day. The story of the demise of native oysters in Carlingford Lough is a good example of how the flat oyster came to be replaced by cupped oysters on the east coast of Ireland.

The written record of flat oysters in Carlingford goes back to 1622. Along with herrings, oysters and mussels from the Lough were the great economic supports of Newry almost from its foundation. In Carlingford and Omeath parishes the oyster money helped pay many of the rents before the Famine. One report indicates that there were 2,000 engaged in the fishery using some 400 boats in 1835. Each boat would get about five long hundreds (50 dozen oysters) a day which, if not sold immediately, were stored in oyster "rings" on the shore and later sold on demand or after they had grown somewhat. Dealers paid eight pence to two shillings a long hundred and sold them in Newry at four shillings and sixpence a long hundred. So the dealers made more than the fishermen, a situation which is no different today! Dredging took place from November to March, with three to five men in a boat, one in charge of the dredge and two or four rowing. Even children were known to collect oysters on the shore at low tide.

The whole of the centre of the Lough was a public bed and therefore open to all comers. Never the less, as we have already mentioned, the Marquis of Anglesey attempted to regulate the fishery as if it were his private property and, in fairness, he appears to have had some success. Stocks were said to have increased up to 1835 due to the elimination of unseasonal fishing and poaching. Oysters were sold on the shore at Omeath with a good deal ending up as far away as Dublin and Belfast. Their reputation for excellence was so great that oysters from Arklow were brought to Omeath and sold there as true Carlingfords. Since many were subsequently exported to Liverpool and Manchester through the port of Warrenpoint where they fetched seven to fifteen shilling a thousand, the deception was hardly noticed.

Stocks were strong, and increasing, in 1830, still significant in 1846, but collapsed between 1850 and 1860. They recovered again after a few years and so did the traditional sales to Liverpool, the English dealers Mussen and Co. and Petrie and Co. being among the biggest buyers. They graded the oysters, taking the larger ones off for immediate resale in England and storing the smaller in

Fig. 59. Oyster parcs at Omeath Co, Louth. Oysters were stored in these enclosures prior to sale. At first they were used for European oysters but towards the end of the nineteenth century they were stocked mainly with American oysters on their way to the British market through Warrenpoint, on the left of the picture and through Greenore.

oyster parcs near Omeath to grow and fatten (Fig. 59). With this approach they could buy oysters of any size at any time, which did no favour at all to the wild stocks. It was estimated that about 235 dredgers were working in 1865. Mussels, too, were being extensively dredged at that time and by 1874 the oyster stocks were apparently dredged out. The owners of private beds, most notably the Woodhouse family of Omeath Park Estate, resorted to imports of flat oysters from Auray in France and from Holland to replenish their beds. This strategy was partially successful and they were able to continue for a while selling flat oysters to the English dealers. An English physician, Dr. John Philpots, writing in 1890 could not praise the Carlingford oyster enough: ". . . .Of all the molluscs it is the best in Ireland; a black-bearded fellow, delicate and of fine flavour, to be eaten in Dublin alternately with the Redbank oyster, at a magnificent establishment in Sackville Street and to be washed down with alternate drafts of brown stout. It is said to want nothing that it should have and to have nothing it should want." They were, in truth, just what the doctor ordered and we are left in no doubt about the great pleasure the good doctor himself took on his metropolitan peregrinations! How we could have allowed such a valuable resource to decline almost to extinction is beyond comprehension.

As Irish flat oyster stocks were declining Mussen and Co. were already selling American cupped oysters (*Crassostrea virginica*) in England to meet the huge demand in the summer months. These were imported in barrels from New York and landed in Liverpool in March and April. Those not required for immediate sale were sent by steamer to Warrenpoint and laid in the oyster parcs near

Omeath (Fig 59) to await the demand of the market once the flat oyster season closed at the end of April. The local owners took up the same idea and started to buy and lay down American cupped oysters on their beds too, where they did remarkably well before being sold on – to Mussen, of course. As the various Irish owners gave up on their licensed oyster beds because of the decline in native flat oysters, Mussen took leases on them. By the 1890s Mussen occupied many of the main Carlingford private oyster beds. The Company then started to import American oysters during the winter months (when oysters survived the Atlantic crossing much better) and laid them down on the Carlingford beds to grow until required in the closed season. In the decade to 1901 they had laid down about thirty million American oysters on the two licensed beds previously owned by the Woodhouse family. By 1903, Mussen and Co. employed sixteen persons, Petrie and Co. employed fourteen and another dealer named McDonald employed eight working these depots – not much compared with the two thousand men who worked the natural beds before 1835.

In this way the great east coast oyster beds – those at Malahide and Sutton Co. Dublin suffered a similar fate – were utterly changed. Mussen and Petrie took leases on the Dublin beds also, using them as depots for both flat and cupped oysters. The extent and variety of oysters stored there one hundred years ago was described by Dr. Browne in 1903: ". . . [The Sutton Creek bed] is used for laying down oysters, chiefly Americans, also oysters from Portugal, and sometimes oysters from Carlingford Lough, Tralee Bay, Arklow, North Sea and France. About 12,000,000 oysters are laid down each season . . . The oysters are sent off three times weekly, from May till September, by rail and steamer, to Messers

Fig. 60. The late Dr. Tony Whilde studying the growth of European oysters in the Clarinbridge fishery in the early 1970s. His were the first serious studies on the native oyster of Galway Bay since the start of the century. Photo: Marianne Whilde.

Mussen and Company, wholesale fish merchants, Liverpool." On the Irish west coast, some oyster growers from England took out licences for beds in Clew Bay and elsewhere, which they stocked with spat dredged from the local public beds. But this was only a delaying tactic and after a short period on the licensed Clew Bay beds the oysters were transferred to the owners' English properties.

Entering the twentieth century Ireland still had some surviving native oyster stocks but these would suffer even further decline, in this case due to an unknown viral disease, during the decades of the twenties and the thirties. By the time that BIM was set up it was beginning to look as if Irish flat oysters were doomed to extinction. Only the Clarinbridge and Tralee public beds, and some other small beds elsewhere were still in reasonable commercial production (Fig. 60).

To experience the true pleasure of the flat oyster, Moran's of the Weir, near Kilcolgan in Co. Galway, is without doubt the incomparable place in which to indulge oneself. That is not mere Galway chauvinism, but an opinion shared by almost all those worldwide who have had the good fortune to visit that *sanctum sanctorum* for aficionados. But be sure to bring your own company – the lonesome oyster is a tasteless one and the more loved the company, the more exquisite the oystering experience. Also, be warned: oystering is not an inexpensive delight any more and you will need deep pockets to sample more than a few dozen or so.

What is not so well known or appreciated is the seasonal rhythm of the oyster in Moran's. My own preference is the Autumn or Harvest oyster. This is the one enjoyed late on a warm, sunny afternoon in midweek during early October before the clocks go back. As the summer ends and the harvest ripens, the oyster again becomes available, new-season fruit of a bounteous sea. The hectic rush of summer trade has passed; so have the festivals; the visitors have largely gone and Moran's reverts to the gentler pace of local custom. A certain, autumnal, repletion is palpable in the air. Then, with the flowing tide swelling the river, the sun making its tired descent into the Bay, the silvery light slowly colouring and diminishing and the chill of the autumn evening coming on, what else but lashings of plump, briny oysters, smooth, delicate and delicious, shared with congenial company, could adequately complement the perfect symmetry of time and place and intimacy? And who but Heaney could express it so wonderfully:

And there we were, toasting friendship,
Laying down a perfect memory
In the cool of thatch and crockery.
. . . I ate the day
Deliberately, that its tang
Might quicken me all into verb, pure verb.
S. Heaney, *Oysters.*

The Christmas oyster is altogether more boisterous, a gay and glitzy fellow. Consumed in cheery company, he gaily glides down gullets to considerable "*oohing*!" and "*aahing*!" and the occasional "*eeking*!" The slurping and guzzling are intercalated with draughts of chilled champagne or Chablis or "whatever you're having yourself". With him all is celebration and gaiety, all Christmas good cheer and merriment, to the accompaniment of clinking glasses and whoops of happy laughter. Tomorrow is temporarily forgotten as today is lived to the full. Let the coming New Year look after itself while we cheerily see out the old and good riddance to it!

The Lenten oyster is of a more thoughtful, melancholic turn, best chewed ruminatively before swallowing. With him, the pint of plain is indeed your only man, provided you are not "off it" for Lent. If you are, it may be possible to take a little "*sos*" around St. Patrick's Day and enjoy, well, a glass if not the whole pint. That's the least the Lenten oyster deserves if it is to sharpen your reflective mood and whet, without satisfying, your penitential palate. In olden times there was little enough left in the family larder by Lent and the oyster played an important role at that difficult time – not necessarily as an item of food, but as an item easily sold for cash that could then be used to meet other more pressing domestic needs. It does us no harm to reflect that things were not always as prosperous for us as they now are. For the Lenten oyster it is often the same. The spring plankton bloom (which plumps him up after the cold winter) has yet to occur and he, too, may be low in reserves, matching our own state. So let us not be too harsh on him as we reflect on "*. . . things past and passing and yet to come*".

The Parting oyster is eaten in late April. It is not a sad parting, more a cheery "*slán tamall*" ("*au revoir*" or "bye for a while!") because we know he has some important personal business to attend to without which we would not see his

Fig. 61.Tom Keenan attends to his oysters in Carlingford Lough where, in the background, the Mountains of Mourne sweep down to the sea. This site was once a famous flat oyster bed but now only the Pacific oyster is grown here.

likes in future generations. He is a jaunty, ritzy fellow and deserves a champagne send-off to speed him on his way. So we wish him a jolly farewell, remembering seasons past and looking forward to many more seasons yet to come. Already the evenings are lengthening and summer beckons; there is an urgency for us all to be about other business and doing other things.

There is no Summer flat oyster. If your need is great, there is the cupped oyster to enjoy. In Moran's be sure it's the locally reared product you get. Oysters take on the characteristics of the area in which they are grown, so local Clarinbridge cupped oysters share the taste and flavour associated with all oysters grown in that region. That advice is good for other places too. In Carlingford, for example, ask for Tom Keenan's oysters, especially his triploids (Fig. 61). You might get them if your host thinks you deserve such special favour. Tom's bed in the Lough was once the property of Burton Bindon, a landowner from Co. Clare who really knew his oysters and where to grow them. It was he who owned the Red Bank oyster bed in Galway Bay and who popularised Redbank oysters in Dublin in the early nineteenth century when he opened a hostelry known as the Redbank Oyster Dive. It was there that the peripatetic Dr. Philpots, quoted earlier, partook of his brown stout and oysters. The establishment also features in Trollope's "Kelly and the O'Kellys". It went upmarket as the Redbank Restaurant and moved to D'Olier Street, where Leopold Bloom remarked on it on his way to Glasnevin, and where it remained in business until 1968. The present successor in title to the name is the Redbank Restaurant in Skerries Co. Dublin and thereby hangs a tale with an ironic twist.

One Monday in 1968, a young man was interviewed for appointment as a commis chef in the original Redbank restaurant in D'Olier Street and was offered the job, starting the following Thursday. When he arrived ready for work on the appointed day it was to find that the restaurant had closed and gone out of business. Commis appointments do not come any shorter than that! Some years later a red-bricked building in Skerries, a branch Bank belonging to the Munster and Leinster Group, was put up for sale. The erstwhile young chef, now fully trained and with an acknowledged reputation, could not resist the irony of taking up, *ag deire thiar thall,* the post to which he had originally been appointed. He bought the old, red Bank building and turned it into the new Redbank Restaurant where he is chef patron. It is now one of the best known establishments of contemporary Irish cuisine, availing especially of the fresh seafood landed at Skerries pier, and the chef patron – Terry McCoy – is justly famous for his fine food and hospitality. His venture is one of those rare happy happenings where a seafood enterprise has taken over a Bank – the opposite is more usual and usually less felicitous.

Burton Bindon's oysters were so well regarded that all oysters from the Clare beds were once called "Burton Bindons" or simply "Redbanks" in mid-nineteenth century Dublin. They were still known as such to Joyce's Leopold Bloom many years later. To meet demand, Bindon was one of the first to take out an oyster bed licence in Carlingford Lough in 1854 at a place adjacent to Mullatee, near Greenore. The Carlingford flat oyster already by then had its own established reputation. As Philpots was to say of it later ". . . it is round and rough as a walnut; opens white, fat and juicy; it is neither too large nor too small, and blends with extreme delicacy the racy sharpness of the sea with the milder flavour of the fish". But even Bindon could not avoid the collapse of the oysters that occurred in the 1850s and he ultimately sold out to Lord Clermont in 1866. The bed eventually came into the possession of the Woodhouse family and then Mussen and Co., who put American cupped oysters there. Tom Keenan farms Pacific cupped oysters there now and the quality is as good as any I have tasted anywhere. Certainly, the fine reputation of Carlingford has not been lost in the long interval between Burton Bindon and Tom Keenan. It has also transferred successfully from the flat to the cupped oyster. Try it in Carlingford; you will not be disappointed. Or try the cupped oysters of Kian Louet who cultivates the same bed and whose produce is available at the Redbank Restaurant. It is a coincidence, of which he was unaware until recently, that when Terry McCoy was seeking a source of the best cupped oysters it was to Kian that he turned, thereby unknowingly re-establishing yet another link with Clare's Burton Bindon the originator of his establishment's famous name. *Viva la* the new brigade, *Viva la* the old one too!

The true lover of the flat oyster knows there is only one proper way to eat them – raw on the half shell, with a squeeze of lemon juice. Anything else is a travesty so no recipe is given here!

Fig. 62. Aerial view of the semi-extensive oyster ponds at Rossmore Oysters in Carrigtwohill, Co. Cork, one of the most impressive oyster farms to be seen anywhere. Photo: David Hugh-Jones.

Chapter 8
OYSTER CULTIVATION

Although we do not concur in the opinion put forward by some as to the extraordinary profits to be made from oyster cultivation, still we believe, if judiciously undertaken, and prudently and perseveringly carried out, that it is profitable and that there is very much to encourage enterprises of the kind.

Report of the Commission on Oyster Culture, Dublin 1870.

EARLY IN THE SECOND HALF of the twentieth century the future of oysters in Ireland did not look at all secure. Generations of over-exploitation had depleted the stocks so that only the beds of Tralee Bay, Galway Bay and Clew Bay were still yielding a half-decent return to the public fisheries. But even in these places, dredging was restricted to a short period of a few weeks, or days, each season. The prospect of Ireland's eventual entry into the European Common Market was being mooted at the time and were we to join, that was bound to increase the export of fish and fish products to continental markets. Therefore BIM commenced the first ever inventory of the Irish shellfish resource. Dr. Eric Edwards (Fig. 63) was engaged for the task in 1967 and Dr. Tony Whilde (Fig. 60) soon joined him in surveying the Galway Bay oyster stocks. The news was, as is often the case, both good and bad. The good news was that the stocks were in better condition than anyone had any right to hope; the bad news was that illegal and excessive fishing was rampant and management of the stocks was non-existent. BIM therefore responded by setting up a new Resource Development Section under Edwards that immediately initiated a two-pronged approach to the management of the Galway oyster beds.

Fig. 63. Dr. Eric Edwards who was employed by BIM to initiate the modern phase of Irish shellfish management around 1970. He undertook the first shellfish and crustacean resource developmental surveys.

First, steps were taken to improve their physical condition by the laying of cultch and other habitat interventions like the removal of starfishes. (Cultch is the name given to the empty shells and other hard material spread on the sea bottom on which oyster spat can settle.) But the more difficult task was that of wresting the initiative from those who, allowed to continue without proper regulation, would drive the resource to extinction by continued over-exploitation and poaching. The challenge was to win community support for the proper management of the resource as a community asset to be harvested and regulated by a local cooperative. Something like that had been tried and had worked in the distant past. What it required was a change in the mind-set of those who, quite rightly, regarded unfettered access to the sea and the sea fisheries as their right in common law but who mistakenly viewed all regulation "from above" (in Ireland "above" usually means Dublin) as unwarranted interference with those rights. Convincing those who held such views required patience, diplomacy and steady application before it would come about, which it did by the end of the century. By then, and after some false dawns, false titles and false figures, the public oyster beds of Galway Bay, and the erstwhile private St. George oyster bed in the same area, were vested in the local community, and local oyster cooperatives were actively engaged in the management and restoration of the oyster stocks. More importantly, the strategy laid the foundations for a new, cooperative and interactive approach to resource management elsewhere. This was to evolve into new concepts like Single Bay Management and Coordinated Local Aquaculture Management (CLAMS), community-led programmes that would come into operation in different areas and on which the future of successful aquacultural enterprises is likely to depend. We will discuss them in a later chapter.

In Cork Harbour matters had taken a different course. This, too, had always been an area of good oyster growth and the native stocks had been strong until the inevitable over-exploitation took its toll. Blackrock appears to have been a hotbed of armed poachers in the late nineteenth century, so much so that one of the oyster bed owners appealed for a gunboat to be stationed in Lough Mahon to curb them. The gunboat never materialized, but the problem abated when one particular poacher turned gamekeeper, bought the licence and made sure that his friends knew it! Still, the Cork oyster stocks continued to decline, were severely depleted by the century's end and were still in a parlous state sixty years later.

Oysters need the company of many other oysters if they are to reproduce successfully. After all, parent oysters do not "pair off" like some higher organisms do.

Individuals change their sex from time to time so that they themselves cannot tell which, or how many, males and females are about the place. When ripe, the females produce millions of eggs but they hold them within their shells attached to the gills. Males release sperm into the water column with gay abandon and as long as the density of oysters is high there is a very good chance that some of it will be drawn into the gills of the ripe females where it will fertilize the eggs. But when the stocks are heavily fished, the density of oysters is reduced and the distance between individuals may be too great for enough active sperm to reach all the females in good time and in satisfactory quality to achieve fertilization. The inevitable result will be that spawning will not be very successful. So, the more oysters in the bed, the greater the potential for successful reproduction!

That observation is the basis for the semi-extensive cultivation of flat oysters by Rossmore Oysters in Cork Harbour for over forty years. The technique is fairly straightforward. Broodstock oysters are laid densely in a seawater pond on a layer of mussel-shell cultch. The oysters breed naturally, aided by the warm conditions and the natural plankton that blooms in the pond. When the resultant spat settle, the cultch is collected, fragmented and re-laid in other nursery ponds where the spat can continue to grow in safety with an abundance of food. Once they have grown beyond the delicate earliest stage, at a size of about five millimetres, they can be transferred to an open sea oyster bed for production. In three to four years they will have reached market size. They can then be lifted, purified in tanks to clear them of grit and other matter and sent off in refrigerated trucks to the packing stations.

In the late 1960s David Hugh-Jones identified a suitable site in the sheltered inlet of Rossmore close by the North Channel public oyster bed (and far from Blackrock!) where he commenced to breed oysters in large ponds excavated for that purpose in the soil of a long peninsula. Hugh-Jones was applying a "low technology" method, first used in the eighteen sixties and later developed in the UK by Dr. H. A. Cole and Dr. Peter Walne. The technique had been largely abandoned during the War and was superceded by artificial hatchery technology after the War had ended. It was not an easy or a cheap strategy to initiate; the extent of excavation undertaken, covering over twenty acres, can be gauged from the picture (Fig. 62). The project started off small with only a single pond. The availability of butyl rubber as a pond liner obviated the need for costly concrete tank construction. The plan also required very large numbers of oysters to be collected together in the pond to simulate a dense natural bed. These adult oysters were brought from Tralee and Galway and were then acclimated to the pond. Now all Hugh-Jones needed was good fortune so that the climate and weather would not frustrate his efforts. Just before spawning was anticipated, mussel-shell cultch was strewn in the pond, the oysters spawned successfully and the enterprise was up and running. It took a further eight years of research and hard work to perfect the methodology and to construct the fine array of ponds that now grace the site. The grand strategy at Rossmore included a plan to produce sufficient oysters to re-stock the North Channel bed and restore it to a self-sustaining natural condition. That would require many millions of oyster spat to be laid down over many years. Hugh-Jones and his staff were not daunted by this prospect and by the mid 1980s production was almost thirteen million young oysters a year. The future was looking bright indeed.

While these developments were progressing at Rossmore the flat oyster was to suffer a cruel blow. The oyster parasite *Bonamia ostreae,* which had earlier decimated the remnant French and English stocks of flat oysters, was discovered in Cork Harbour in 1987 and later in Galway and Clew Bays. It threatened to do to Irish oysters what it had done to oyster stocks elsewhere in Europe. Reports of its presence in Ireland were the worst of all possible news for some producers. Rossmore Oysters really took a blow – of 400 baskets dredged off the open-water growing ground only eight baskets of live oysters were harvested! Fortunately, on a wider, national scale, a developing, pro-active attitude to the resource had started to take hold among the communities engaged in the shellfisheries. Therefore the necessary prudent management precautions and rapid regulatory response needed to prevent the damage becoming a full-blown disaster were quickly implemented and supported. Restrictions were placed on the transfer of oysters between sites and survey programmes were set in place to monitor the parasite's dispersal. *Bonamia* was indeed a severe blow but, by these prompt and appropriate actions, not a fatal one. It has been successfully restricted to the three sites originally affected and it has not transferred to new areas. In Cork, Rossmore Oysters, having turned to cupped oysters in the worst years of the late 1980s, returned to flat oysters again in the nineties with an attempt to breed a disease resistant strain. Production is now on the increase again and hopes are high that resistance can be significantly enhanced. Customers all over the world are again enjoying Cork oysters in the freshest, purest state. Rossmore is today one of Ireland's major exporters of flat and of cupped oysters and the best example of semi-extensive flat oyster cultivation to be seen anywhere. Recovery of the other flat oyster stocks will be slow and they may never again approach their previous abundance. But they are still with us and, thankfully, seem to be holding their own.

But if Bonamiosis were fated to happen, the timing of its occurrence, at least, was not entirely the worst. It alerted the coastal community to the vulnerability of all shellfish stocks to natural and man-made hazards. It stimulated resource surveys at other sites that confirmed just how low stock levels had fallen. The public oyster bed at Tralee, for instance, was producing about 1,000 tonnes a year in the 1970s. This had fallen to about eight tonnes a year by 1985 – and Tralee never had Bonamiosis! The alert galvanized the new shellfish cooperatives that had been emerging since the late 1970s. It became clear that the only sure way forward for the shellfisheries involved management and cultivation rather than continued, unregulated exploitation. Some communities turned to the remaining stocks of flat oysters with new development plans. Others began to look further afield. The intensive artificial production of the Japanese, or Pacific, cupped oyster *Crassostrea gigas* on a commercial scale had already been successfully mastered elsewhere and was proving to be both profitable and reliable. It would lead eventually to the cultivation of that species all over the world. The promise of a similar reliable, artificial technique for intensive spawning and rearing of flat oysters on a commercial scale, which was being actively researched in the Shellfish Laboratory in Carna at the time and that had seemed to be imminent since 1972, was not about to be realized. The flat oyster was proving to be not at all an easy organism to grow. So, Irish eyes turned to cupped oysters, as others had, and they did not have far to turn.

Cupped oysters had already saved the French oyster industry not once, but twice. The Portuguese variety, *Crassostrea angulata,* was introduced widely to France in the nineteenth century where it replaced the stocks of flat oysters that had been devastated through over-exploitation. By the 1950s it sustained an industry of 100,000 tonnes in France and it was the main oyster species in production there. The Portuguese oyster is a well-travelled species. It was first reported in the estuary of the River Tagus near Lisbon around 1800, which begs the question as to how it got there? Scientific studies in the last few years confirm that it is genetically very close to the *Crassostrea gigas* cupped oysters found around Hong Kong in China. The old Portuguese trading colony of Macao is in the same general area and it is tempting to conclude that the oyster was brought from there to Lisbon fortuitously, as an encrustation on the bottoms of trading ships or deliberately, stored in casks as fresh food for the crews. On docking in Lisbon the dregs of the casks would be emptied into the Tagus, or the ships' bottoms would be scraped. It soon spread from Lisbon to the north of Portugal and Spain, sometimes being deliberately introduced to new areas for the purpose of propagation. It was first introduced to Ireland, and Ireland to it, in 1880 when oyster growers imported it from France. It grew well enough in places like Sligo Bay to be imported sporadically until the end of the century. But it did not become acclimated here as it did in France, probably because Irish conditions were too cold for it to spawn naturally.

Even as Edwards and Whilde were surveying the Galway flat oyster stocks between 1967 and 1972, the French stocks of the Portuguese oyster were succumbing to a viral disease that effectively eradicated them entirely by 1973. The French growers resorted to large-scale imports of the Pacific cupped oyster *Crassostrea gigas* from Canada and also directly from Japan. This species established itself well and thrived under French conditions, thereby saving the French oyster industry for a second time. Today, it is the principal oyster grown in France, it spawns naturally in many French bays and it is easily propagated artificially in hatcheries where that course is necessary. Small numbers of flat oysters are still marketed in France whenever they can be had, which is often when supplies arrive from Irish exporters. The great days of *Crassostrea angulata* are long gone and that species is now largely confined to the south coasts of Spain and Portugal.

The success of the introduction of *Crassostrea gigas* to France after 1973 augured well for its introduction to Ireland where it arrived by a circuitous route. Pacific oysters had been introduced from Japan to Canada early in the twentieth century. They acclimated well and grew strongly at quite low temperature (around 15 degrees). Breeding stocks became well established in British Columbia. Adult samples from these were imported into Britain in 1964 where they were artificially bred at the Shellfish Research Station in Conwy, North Wales. Their offspring were used in early growth trials in England.

By 1970 the Conwy staff had mastered their artificial production and in 1972 descendants of these were imported from the Conwy laboratory to the Shellfish Laboratory Carna for breeding purposes and for trials under Irish conditions. Here they proved to be as successful as they had elsewhere and, in addition, they did not breed under Irish conditions in the wild. This latter was an important observation. It meant that they would not get "out of hand" by uncontrolled breeding, which might have made them serious competitors for the stricken native flat oyster stocks. Irish growers hesitated no longer. They imported large numbers of cupped oyster spat and oyster farms sprung up all around the south, west and north coasts.

Fig. 64. Cupped oysters do not breed naturally in Ireland and have to be produced artificially or imported. Here a bowl of French cupped oyster spat is offered for sale to Irish shellfish farmers at an annual spat fair. This dish holds about 5,000 oysters.

From this small beginning, imports of spat of Pacific oysters to Ireland were to expand, first from Britain and later on from France and the Channel Islands. The prospect of commercially producing spat from broodstock grown here led to the setting up of a number of Irish oyster hatcheries. Their aim was to service the Irish market with "home-grown" Irish cupped oyster spat. But producers in France and Britain had a head start on the Irish hatcheries, and bigger home markets, so that they were able to supply the emergent Irish industry at prices way below those of the local Irish producers. Despite the risks associated with the import of non-native spat – if one buys from elsewhere, one buys into the pathogen and parasite regime of one's supplier – the Irish growers turned to the English and French suppliers for seed. Today, almost all Irish-grown cupped oysters start off their life as imported spat, some of it wild naturally spawned spat from France and some hatchery-produced in France or the UK (Fig. 64). To borrow a phrase, if the French seed oyster industry now sneezes, the Irish oyster industry immediately gets pneumonia! This is not a happy situation from an Irish viewpoint.

Unlike flat oysters, which change sex regularly and often and in which the females incubate the earliest embryonic stages on their gills, Pacific oysters are the proverbial doddle when it comes to reproduction. They do not often change sex and they release the eggs and sperm directly into the water column where they combine to produce the larvae that are then easily collected. Give adults a few weeks of warm conditions (around 25 degrees) and plenty of food and they will spawn with utter abandon in uninhibited profusion. One female will produce many millions of eggs, so there is never a shortage of raw material, no matter how few females one uses.

The swimming larvae are grown for two weeks in large tanks of heated seawater supplied with specially grown algae. They are as fastidious in what they will eat as the adults are and only a few species of micro-algae are acceptable to them. Special collecting surfaces are placed in the larval tanks just before settlement so that as many spat as are needed can be collected as they settle. Newly settled spat are scraped from the settlement surfaces and grown in what are called "nurseries". These are special tanks or flumes or special containers called "upwellers", where the spat are fed and can grow and strengthen under properly controlled artificial conditions until they are large enough to be put out in the sea in small-mesh bags. Once they are about five millimetres in size they are large enough to be sold on to the shellfish farmers for "finishing" in fish farms. The farmers place them in mesh bags that are fixed to trestles set in the sea low down on the shore (Figs. 65 and 66). Here they grow, feeding on the natural plankton. The bags are changed as they grow, larger mesh bags replacing the smaller, as the oysters get bigger. If the mesh is too small, water cannot get into the bags very easily especially when the mesh becomes clogged with settling natural algae. Some farmers put winkles into the bags to graze the settling algae and keep the bags free-flowing.

Life in a bag is easy. Being held up off the ground on a trestle ensures that starfish do not get their sticky hands, or more correctly their arms, on them. As the trestles are normally set low down on the shore the oysters spend most of their time under water and feeding. The bags are turned regularly to shake up the oysters (Fig. 67). This prevents them clumping together and helps to keep the bags free of weed. At intervals the bags are brought ashore (Fig. 68), emptied and the oysters separated, graded by size, then re-bagged or sold on to market. The whole growth process, from 5 millimetre spat to market-sized oyster, will take from 15 months to maybe two or three years, depending on growing conditions and on the general environment of the area and the precise site.

From a practical viewpoint, the oyster farm site needs to be suitable to set and hold the trestles and other structures used on the lower shore. It needs to be safe, workable for some hours around low tide and free from navigational and recreational hazards, especially if it is a large farm (Fig. 69). Generally, large shallow bays that have extensive expanses of silty sand exposed at low tide, with good but not excessive tidal flow and low exposure to strong winds will be suitable if there is good access to them and a reasonably good infrastructure in the area.

Fig. 65. Oyster bags set on trestles in long rows in Dungarvan Bay.

Fig. 66. Trestles with oyster bags attached on a farm in Carlingford Lough.

Fig. 67. Oyster bags are turned regularly to ensure that the oysters do not become cemented together and to keep down algal growth on the mesh. This farm is located in Dungarvan Bay.

Fig. 68. Oyster bags are collected at intervals and returned by tractor to the farm premises for grading and re-bagging. The scene here is at Bannow Bay, Co. Wexford. When the bags are taken up, the trestles are less easily seen from afar. Photo: Brian O'Loan.

Fig. 69. A very large area of Bannow Bay is given over to oyster farming. Photo: Brian O'Loan.

Where a site is otherwise particularly suitable, the absence of infrastructure may not be a problem: one of the great successes of aquaculture in Ireland is the boost it has given to the infrastructural development of many remote localities that might otherwise never have developed as they have. But the outstanding feature of a good site is an abundance of suitable planktonic food and benign water temperatures. Without these, growth and fattening will be poor. Not many people realize that the planktonic food resource, the microscopic plants and animals that make the sea a dilute soup that sustains the filter-feeding organisms living on the shore and the sea bottom, is not inexhaustible. This food resource is very definitely finite and its abundance determines the "carrying capacity" of a bay or inlet, that is, the maximum biomass of living organisms that the bay can support. Thankfully, most Irish bays have not yet exhausted their carrying capacity but there is no room for complacency. Many French oyster localities are exceeding their carrying capacity with consequent detrimental effects on their cultivated shellfish stocks.

There are stringent regulations regarding water quality in all areas in which shellfish for human consumption may be grown. Areas designated "A" are pristine and shellfish may be sold and consumed directly from them without any prior purification treatment. Areas designated "B" are also of very high quality but shellfish must be depurated – allowed to cleanse in tanks of clean flowing seawater for about 48 hours – before they are finally sold for human consumption.

It is an obvious, but unfortunate, fact of modern life that much of our food needs to be treated in a precautionary manner like this. In many cases it reflects the extremely high standards people expect their food to guarantee today, rather than any insurmountable problem associated with the growing site or with the food item itself. Most of our shellfish sites are graded A or B and strict monitoring ensures that we can have the utmost confidence in the output of our shellfish farms. Of course we strive continuously to have all waters graded A, not just to cultivate shellfish but to affirm our desire to have the best quality marine environment for everyone.

Production of cupped oysters in Ireland increased from 400 tonnes to 6,500 tonnes in the decade from 1989 to 1999. Today it exceeds 11,000 tonnes and involves over 250 separate farms employing more than 700 persons. It is nowhere near its maximum capacity yet. One third of all production occurs in the southeast, mainly in Bannow Bay, Ballyheigue Bay, Waterford Estuary and Dungarvan Bay. Here, without question, the environmental conditions for growth are better than elsewhere in the country. However, cupped oysters are fast growers and, since different markets demand different kinds of oysters, other places are not to be dismissed for oyster cultivation. About one quarter of Irish production occurs in the Cork, Kerry and Clare region, and other notable centres include Greater Galway Bay, Clew Bay, Greater Sligo Bay and Carlingford Lough.

In Galway Bay, cupped oysters are now being grown in extensive culture. For this, half-grown oysters are seeded onto the oyster ground and left there to grow under natural conditions for one or more years. After that they are lifted using a modern oyster harvesting dredger, the largest such vessel in Europe (Fig. 70). Allowing oysters to grow in the wild like this makes good use of the beds and the available food resource of the Bay. If it proves a commercial success, extensive cultivation of oysters is likely to be taken up at other Irish localities also.

For eating, cupped oysters are available all year round and in all parts of the country. How one enjoys them is entirely a personal matter, although it is hard to beat them stuffed in a good fillet steak in the dish sometimes called "devils on horseback". But eaten raw, like flat oysters, they are also very good even if one cannot eat quite the same number as one would of flat oysters. Now that production techniques are well in hand, (although more remains to be done by way of mechanization and advanced husbandry) the attention of some

Fig. 70. A modern oyster-harvesting dredger operates in Galway Bay. It is the largest vessel of its kind in Europe. It raises and grades cupped oysters growing in extensive culture in the Bay. This bed was originally a flat oyster bed that is now devoid of native stock. The extensive cultivation of cupped oysters promises to restore oyster growing in Galway Bay to very significant levels.

enterprises is turning to the creation of new frozen, breaded and coated oyster products. Cupped oysters, whether Portuguese, Pacific or American, lend themselves well to such novelties and to innovative cooking. They are much richer and creamier than their European flat cousins and for that reason they are often cooked before eating:

For breakfast or for supper, on the under shell or upper,
Of dishes he's the daisy, and of shellfish he's the star.
We try him as they fry him, and even as they pie him;
We're partial to him luscious in a roast;
We boil him and broil him, we vinegar-and-oil him,
And O! he is delicious stewed with toast.
We eat him with tomatoes, and with salad with potatoes
Nor look him o'er with horror when he follows the coldslaw;
And neither does he fret us if he marches after lettuce
And abreast of cayenne pepper when his majesty is raw.

Anonymous, The Detroit Free Press, 1889.

There is no better way to celebrate the excellence of Irish cupped oysters – along with other prime Irish products – than to feast on "Carlingford Oysters Táin Bó" in Terry McCoy's Redbank Restaurant in Skerries, Co. Dublin. As one gourmet remarked, if the men of Ulster could have cooked like this, Connaught's Queen Maedhbh would have come to County Louth to dine rather than to steal the *Dú Cuailnge* (The Brown Bull of Cooley) and Ferdia might never have died at the hands of his best friend Cú Chulainn. It is a truly magnificent dish fit for heroes; instructions are given in the accompanying box.

Carlingford Oysters Táin Bó

INGREDIENTS

6 Carlingford oysters. 1½ pts. fish stock. 2 black sole x 1 lb. 3 eggs. 1 pt. Cream. Salt and pepper. 4 strands carrageen moss. 2 measures Cooley whiskey. Seaweed. 10 broad leaves of spinach (wild spinach if available). 1 measure of Guinness stout. 1 clove garlic crushed. ½ lb. Wild salmon fillet. ½ lb. unsalted butter. Teaspoon rich soy sauce. 4 asparagus spears. Teaspoon oyster sauce

GARNISH

2 carrots, 4 potatoes.

METHOD

Open the oysters and reserve the juices. Fillet the soles and place the four smaller fillets in a food processor with four of the raw oysters and the salmon fillet. Blend until roughly mixed. Add the garlic and seasoning. Separate the whites and yolks of the eggs and add all the whites and one yolk to the blended mixture.

Further puree until smooth and then add ½ pint of cream slowly blending until the mixture is bound together in a smooth paste.

Simmer 1 pint of fish stock, add the spinach leaves and blanch. Remove the blanched leaves, cool and place them on the sole fillets. Now spread some of the oyster and fish mousse on the four fillets and roll up from the tail end. Skewer with a cocktail stick or wrap in cling film to hold in place.

Place some of the oyster mousse into two buttered moulds or old teacups; place the remaining oysters on top and then the last of the mousse. Place the moulds and the stuffed soles into the simmering fish stock with the strands of carrageen moss and cook until firm to the touch.

Mould the garnish vegetables into attractive presentable shapes and place into the simmering stock until cooked.

Meanwhile, in a separate pan reduce the remaining fish stock to make a fish cream sauce using the remaining cream and unsalted butter. Heat a small pan and flame off the alcohol from the whiskey. Add some of the cooking stock from the pot with the fillets and the vegetable juices to the whiskey and reduce a little. Now add some of the fish cream and the Cooley Mountain Whiskey Sauce is made.

In a bowl blend the two remaining egg yolks with two egg cups of Guinness and some rich soy sauce and oyster sauce and the reserved oyster juices mentioned at the start. Whisk into the remaining fish cream and the Brown Bull of Cooley Guinness Sauce is ready.

Palace the Guinness sauce in the centre of a plate and the whiskey sauce around the edge. Feather lightly. Place the oyster mould in the centre and then carve the sole fillets and arrange around the oyster mould.

Arrange the green, white and gold vegetable garnish and present.

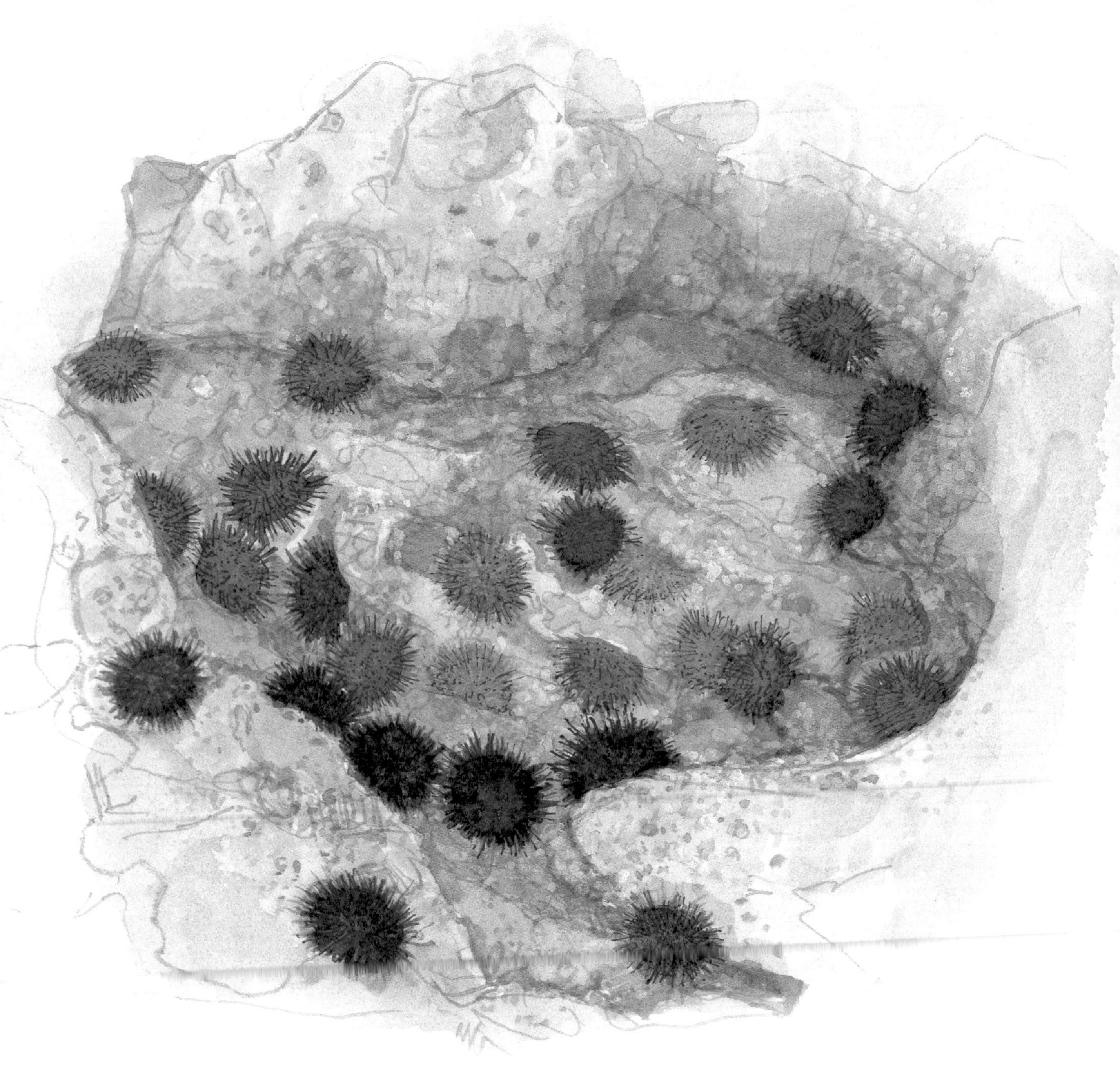

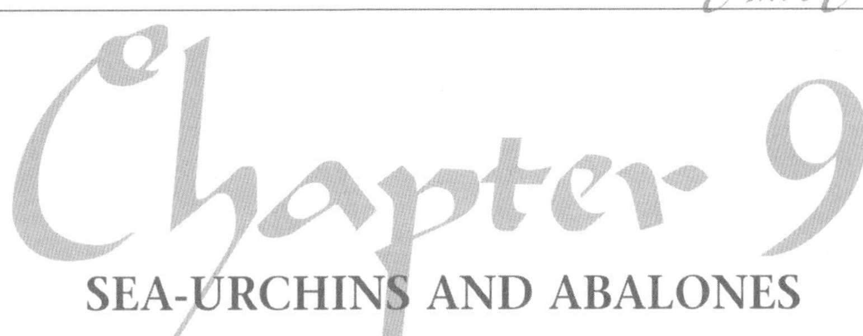

SEA-URCHINS AND ABALONES

If you are familiar with the limestone rock pools of Ireland's west coast, at low tide you will have noticed something missing. A few years ago they were there in some numbers. But now, just empty hemispherical hollows in the rock mark where the purple sea urchin used to live. What has happened?

Friends of the Irish Environment, 2003.

So far we have progressed through the species in order of increasing cultivation, from those that are harvested but not (yet) cultivated i.e. the limpets and winkles, through those that are cultivated by the collection and rearing of naturally spawned juveniles (mussels and scallops), to those in which hatchery production is still under development (European oysters) or is already well-mastered (some clams); and on finally to those where artificial hatchery production is an absolute essential for their production in Ireland (Pacific oysters). Now we come to the "alpha and the omega" species of this shellfish progression. These are, respectively, the purple sea-urchin, *Paracentrotus lividus* and the abalones or ormers *Haliotis tuberculata* and *Haliotis discus hannai*. But first we need a few words of explanation.

The abalone is a true Mollusc, that is, a true shellfish. It is a member of the molluscan class Gastropoda like the winkles, limpets and whelks. But the purple urchin is not a shellfish (a mollusc) in the zoological sense at all. It is a member of an entirely different Phylum of animals called the Phylum Echinodermata. This group, the name of which means "spiny-skinned", includes the starfishes, the sea cucumbers and the echinoids, the latter group being the one to which the sea-urchin belongs. But the fact that it is not a shellfish is no barrier to its inclusion among them when it comes to EU regulations. In so far as it is governed by EU directive 91/492/EEC laying down health conditions for the production and sale

Fig. 71. Living purple urchins.

Fig. 72. Algal growing tanks at John Chamberlain's hatchery in Dunmanus Bay Co. Cork where the growth process is largely automated. The production of adequate amounts of suitable algae is one of the most demanding tasks in artificial shellfish cultivation.

of live bivalve molluscs, the sea-urchin is regarded as a bivalve, nature and nurture notwithstanding. This is hardly the first or the only instance where European regulations seem strange. But if the law can be an ass, why can the sea-urchin not be a bivalve? It certainly is marketed and consumed as "shellfish", as indeed are prawns, crabs and lobsters. They, too, are not true shellfish at all but members of the Phylum Arthropoda ("jointed legs") to which spiders and insects belong! On such zoological distinctions long academic careers have been enjoyed and many generations of students have been entertained when they were not put to sleep. From the shellfish industry viewpoint such zoological niceties are moot.

But why call these species the "alpha" and the "omega" of the shellfish story?

ALPHA

Paracentrotus lividus, in Irish *Cuán mara dubh* (Fig. 71), is a native of the west and southwest coasts of Ireland. Here it exists as the northernmost populations of a species that is more typically a southern resident, common on French, Spanish and Portuguese coasts and in the Mediterranean Sea. Its presence with us is a result of the ameliorating influence of the North Atlantic Drift on our marine fauna and flora. It lives in lower shore pools and down to sublittoral depths of about three metres. In the sublittoral and in tidal pools, the urchin lives free on the bottom since there is no risk of desiccation and scouring by wave action is reduced. Here it feeds on large algae and grazes beds of the sea grass *Zostera*. When it lives in the intertidal zone it burrows into soft rocks, using its teeth to form a depression in which it lives, sheltered and protected from wind (desiccation) and wave (dislodgement). As it grows it increases the size of the depression, which may be deepened into a burrow from which it is impossible to retrieve the animal. Such burrows can permeate soft rock like the limestone pavements of the coast of Clare. The urchin is not alone in this behaviour: Brendan Keegan of the University in Galway has recorded five species of shellfish that are grinding and dissolving away the limestone coast of the Burren, honeycombing and crumbling its rocks to such an extent that they come to resemble, in a way, pumice stone. Such eviscerated rocks lose their weight and are easily tossed high on the storm shore by wave action. It is an irony that as we enjoy eating their cousins they are chomping away at the very bedrock of the country! Earlier on we saw that ancestral shellfish gave us much of the carboniferous limestone that covers large parts of Ireland; here we see their descendants taking it back.

Their long, sharp spines make urchins an unwelcome presence for those children and adults who like pottering barefooted in tidal pools or who might be tempted to collect them by hand. This protection is, of course, exactly what the spines are meant to achieve. Although well known in our fauna for a long time, there is no tradition of eating urchins in Ireland until very recent times and then only by a few gourmets. They were, therefore, one of the very few Irish natural resources that was neither valued nor harvested nor cultivated nor eaten. To all Irish culinary and commercial intents, they did not exist until the end of the twentieth century. It is in this sense that the urchin is the alpha species, the Irish native that had no previous history but is now an important item of shellfish commerce in the modern generation: truly a species that has come in from the cold.

Historically the only large mammal predator that succeeded in enjoying them in its diet is the common otter, *Lutra lutra*, called in Irish *an dobharchú* or *an madra uisce* ("the water hound". Strangely enough, the generic Irish name for the urchin, *Cuán mara,* means "little sea hound"). Coastal otters are opportunistic fish eaters normally, but they eat urchins when necessity dictates, especially in the winter months. It is at that time that the urchins are at their most nourishing because their reproductive organs, which form the bulk of the animal, are ripe and full. So the otters' seasonal feeding behaviour seems to justify the epithet "sagacious" sometimes applied to them.

Other examples of mammals feeding on shore invertebrates are less authentic. Birds, on the other hand, are past masters at dining on shore animals and are occasionally a major threat to shellfish enterprises. Michael Viney records a singular account of field mice apparently eating winkles, but that report was never confirmed. The story of the fox and the limpet, on the other hand, is so widely recorded in so many different cultures that it is almost a kind of primitive "urban myth" of the seashore. In this, the fox is said to have attempted to eat the limpet as it moved over the rocks feeding at low tide. The fox inserted his tongue under the shell, whereupon the limpet closed down tightly and remained closed until the tide came in and the poor fox was drowned, trapped by its tongue! The episode is sometimes recounted with a rat or a mouse as the unfortunate victim. Whatever its value as a morality tale, the story has no supporting evidence and in truth is a most unlikely occurrence. But in the case of the otter and the urchin, scientific evidence from James Fairley, Ireland's foremost mammalogist, leaves no doubt about the accuracy of the observation.

We came late to the harvesting of sea-urchins, but when we did, we did so with a vengeance. Fishing first commenced in 1948 but at a level so low as to be unrecorded in official statistics. Only the roe – the female reproductive organ or gonad – is eaten. This of course means that there is no incentive for the fisherman to leave sexually mature animals in place so that they can spawn and reproduce their kind. After spawning the urchin is of no culinary or commercial value.

The collapse of the stocks in Brittany around 1970 created a shortage in the continental markets where the urchin – called *oursin* in French – is highly prized by gourmets. Within a few years Ireland had joined the European Union, an event that precipitated not only the "clam boom" mentioned earlier but also a boom in the much more valuable sea-urchin fishery. Stocks were literally plundered all along the southwest and the west coasts both by shore collecting and by scuba diving. In the early 1970s, rarely a week passed without an Aer Lingus flight departing from Cork to Paris laden with live sea urchins destined for the Rungis market. The bonanza continued until 1976. Many a tidy fortune was made and many a fine bungalow was built with its proceeds. Inevitably the landings of urchins went into severe decline from a peak of 375 tonnes – about 14 million individuals – in 1976 to less than one tonne in the year 2000.

Brendan Keegan estimated the number of purple urchins in Muckinish inlet in Galway Bay in 1972 at 1,600 individuals per square metre. They were piled one upon the other in every available space. Today there are no urchins at all in the locality. Similar depredation of the stocks is apparent at other accessible sites all along the Clare coast. Even those with no interest in fish and fisheries could hardly fail to notice the change on the ground that resulted: the urchin has, in many places, disappeared as a common intertidal animal. Tidal pools now very rarely have big stocks of urchins, or else they contain only small individuals safely burrowed into the rock. There is hardly any need now to warn paddling children of the danger of standing on a sea-urchin.

We have no convincing knowledge of the health of the deeper water stocks, but the fact that much of the earlier depredation was caused by scuba diving gives little confidence that they have avoided the decline suffered by their intertidal brothers. Nowadays in Ireland it is illegal to collect shellfish or any other species by scuba diving, but the horse may have bolted already as far as the urchin is concerned.

Since early in the twentieth century, urchins were used to teach embryology to students of medicine and biology. Their eggs and sperm are easily collected from ripe individuals and fertilization under experimental conditions is very easy. It is a short path from this to devising conditions suitable for the mass production of urchin larvae with a view to artificial cultivation. Short it may be, but easy it is not. Unlike bivalve molluscs, post-larval urchins are grazing animals. Both the juveniles and adult can only eat algae that are attached to surfaces, whereas the filter feeding bivalves eat algae that are suspended in the water. This seemingly minor difference has major implications for hatchery production. It means that the proper algal species need to be coated onto solid surfaces to form a living film of food for the post-larval urchins, thereby creating another, difficult, step in the production cycle. When they have grown beyond the early juvenile stage they can be weaned onto larger algae – macro-algae – that are easier to procure and require no preparation. Although Irish urchin cultivation was pioneered by Paul Leighton and Tomás Burke in Carna over a decade ago, and its broad outlines are now understood, the fine details of the process still remain as much an art as a science and the commercialisation stage has been slow to advance.

Fig. 73. A long natural pool is sub-divided into two stepped chambers to hold small urchins restocked from the hatchery. The urchins will grow to maturity in the pools to which natural algae or artificial food will be added as necessary. Photo: Tomás Burke.

Dulse or dillisk – *Palmaria palmata*, that is *duileasc* or *creathnach* in Irish – is said to be the preferred diet of urchins but it is not always available in abundance in the wild. John Chamberlain, who pioneers the commercialisation process at his hatchery in Dunmanus Bay (Fig. 72), finds that juveniles will happily consume the film of diatoms that occurs naturally on Laminaria fronds, while the adults will consume the Laminaria frond itself. This certainly helps with the nurture of juveniles that would otherwise need artificial food or impossible amounts of dulse. (There is extensive international research underway on artificial diets that can be used to "bulk up" the adult urchins' gonads.) Chamberlain's enterprise is important in other respects too. Not only is he producing urchins for commercial sale he is also taking the lead in restocking the natural environment with seed urchins as a form of extensive culture. This is a common practice in Japan but represents both a social and technological innovation in Ireland.

Once the juveniles are about 15 millimetres in diameter they can be placed out in tanks or in natural rock pools that are stocked with laminaria, or scattered free on the sea bottom. The animals fend for themselves from then on, until they are large enough to be harvested. In this way, impoverished natural stocks can be enhanced and new areas seeded with urchins so that there is some prospect that aquaculture will begin to undo some of the damage that excessive fishing has inflicted in the wild. In West Cork, long narrow clefts in the rocky sandstone coast can be easily sub-divided into longitudinal stepped pools suitable to retaining the urchins and to which supplementary algae or artificial food can be added as necessary (Fig. 73). Such semi-extensive cultivation is as close to natural production as can be achieved and it promises to be a useful new approach to urchin production in the southwest. At present there are three hatcheries operating in Ireland, at Bere Island and Dunmanus in Cork and at Castlegregory in County Kerry. These are expected to produce up to two tonnes of urchins this year – small by historical landings from the wild, but a great advance in aquaculture development.

There are no Irish recipes for urchins. The French are the great aficionados of them so it is fitting that we give the French manner of eating them as graphically described in the *Nouveau Larousse Gastronomique*. As we can see from the accompanying box, for the true gourmet "less is more": only the sexual organs are eaten and these mainly raw.

OMEGA

Abalones (Fig. 74) are absent from the Irish marine fauna. Their nearest occurrence to our latitude in Europe is in the Channel Islands where the local species *Haliotis tuberculata*, called the ormer, occurs on rocky shores. To our eyes the environment of the Irish coast appears quite suitable for it, but historically the species itself does not seem to agree! It is almost unthinkable that such a close neighbour would never once have chanced to come to our shores, either as a larva or an adult, in the course of millennia of evolutionary time. It is much more likely that it did, either naturally in the water column or carried passively on boats or on flotsam, but that some aspect of our environment did not suit its reproductive habits. For that reason it would not have become established here and would have remained a stranger to us. There are two old records prior to 1820 of ormer shells being dredged in Irish coastal waters. But it is not certain that these were living specimens so they cannot really be taken as good evidence that the species ever lived here naturally. Aquaculture has altered all that and now the species is under cultivation here. Not only the European species, but also a Pacific species has been introduced from Japan and as we shall see they are doing well in intensive culture.

Fig. 74. Pacific abalones attached to perforated plastic piping in the Carna Shellfish Laboratory. The abalones avoid light and live under the plastic during the day. At night they move about the tank, feeding on algae that settle on the plastic or that Ciarán Moylan, pictured here, adds to the tanks.

Abalones are gastropod molluscs, related to limpets. Like them, the abalones are grazers of seaweed and as such might be expected to find life good on the seaweed-rich west coast of Ireland. John Mercer of the Carna Shellfish Laboratory thought so in 1976 when he introduced the species from Guernsey, observing the stringent quarantine conditions laid down for introductions of new species. As these conditions would not permit the adult broodstock to be laid out in the wild, the task facing the Laboratory staff was to spawn the imported founders in the hatchery and produce disease-free offspring without delay. Bob Latouche and his team succeeded marvellously with the task in 1977. In ensuing years they perfected the hatchery technique and developed feeding regimes so that adequate seed abalones could be provided to shellfish farmers for on-growing trials under local culture conditions. Since the species does not appear to breed unaided under Irish environmental conditions it will always be necessary to have hatchery production if commercial abalone farming is to succeed.

Eggs and sperm are collected from the parents and artificial fertilization is achieved. The larvae that hatch from the eggs live only a very short time, about three days, in the water column and they do not feed during this period. Then they settle on solid surfaces placed as collectors in the larval bins. The settled post-larvae, like those of the urchin, are grazers of micro-algae attached to solid surfaces, which as we said, adds greatly to the difficulty and cost of seed production. A film of suitable micro-algae must be grown on the settlement surfaces before they are introduced into the larval bins. The post-larvae remain feeding on these until they

Fig. 76. Detail of the shell decoration of the Curraghmore shell house. Note how fresh, brilliantly colourful and iridescent the shells still are.

Fig. 75. Inside surface of the shell house in the grounds of Curraghmore House in Portlaw, Co. Waterford. Every square centimetre of the surface is covered with shells, carefully attached over 250 years ago.

Fig. 77. Garden wall in Goleen, Co. Cork, decorated with native Irish shells.

are about 5 millimetres in size. Soon after that they develop pronounced nocturnal and light-avoidance behaviour and at this stage they can be weaned on to the macro-algae that will form the adult diet. Just like the urchin, the food most preferred by the adult European abalone – the red alga *Palmaria palmata* – is not one of the commonest species available in Ireland. Alternatives had to be found, and they were, but these did not result in good growth. How often we have to learn the lesson that the animal knows best what is good for it!

In 1979 John Mercer had assisted with the introduction of the European lobster to Japan and as a *"quid pro quo"* he asked his Japanese colleagues at Sanriku University to make their abalone – *Haliotis discus hannai* – available to him. So, in 1986, this Japanese species was introduced from the Pacific Ocean to the Shellfish Laboratory Carna, again under strict quarantine, and the staff had to set about learning the ways of the oriental stranger. These were not quite so easily mastered but success did come eventually and the species was spawned successfully. The preferred seaweed food of the adults is kelp, especially the genus *Laminaria,* of which we really do have plenty in Ireland. In laboratory trials growth of the Japanese abalone was about 10% better than that of the European species so it looked like a very suitable candidate for Irish growing conditions. Adult abalones are shy, nocturnal animals and they prefer low light intensity. During the day they rest under artificial shelters that must be placed in the culture tanks if they are to thrive. These can be sections of pipe or any other structure under which the animal can hide but still move about. They feed at night on fresh algae added to the tanks.

The growth and performance of Pacific abalone under commercial fish farming conditions are still being evaluated but if they live up to expectations they promise to make an important contribution to Irish shellfish exports. Prices in Continental markets can be as high as 35 euro per kilogram, so their potential value is quite enormous. In gastronomic terms, the abalone is much sought after especially in Japan and its shell, too, is of value as an object of some beauty. An early example of its decorative use can be found in the embellishment of the little-known shell house at Curraghmore Estate in Co. Waterford (Fig. 75) that was painstakingly decorated by Katherine Countess of Tyrone in 1750. The shells were imported for the project and their variety, iridescence and brilliance are absolutely astonishing today some two hundred and fifty years after they were first put in place (Fig. 76). Shell houses and shell cabinets went through phases of great popularity in the seventeenth and eighteenth centuries but they have largely fallen from fashion in our time. When building the outer wall of his garden in recent years, one homeowner in Goleen, Co. Cork did not hesitate to decorate it with a variety of native Irish shells that still grace the structure today (Fig 77). The house is near Rock Island in Crookhaven Harbour, which was once a centre for the export of Irish shellfish to Brittany, so the adornment is not inappropriate.

Sea-Urchin

There are few recipes for preparing the sea-urchin. It is chiefly eaten, lightly boiled, like an egg. Cook it in salted boiling water, drain, open by cutting with scissors on the concave side (where the sea-urchin's mouth is situated), drain it completely, throwing out the excremental part, then dip buttered morsels of bread into the shell.

In the region of Marseilles, where sea-urchins are considered a delicacy, they are eaten out of the shell, as described, but uncooked. They are opened, washed (in sea water if possible) and buttered sippets of bread are dipped into the yellow substance clinging to the walls of the shell.
It is said that sea-urchin has great restorative powers.
Its taste, when cooked, is not unlike crayfish.

Fig. 78. Crookhaven Harbour, Co. Cork. This was once an important harbour on the shipping route from Europe to the New World. Crookhaven village is on the right. The large island in the background is Rock Island. The white structure at the waterside on the Island marks the premises of the Oulhen family who exported shellfish from here to Brittany in the mid twentieth century (see Fig. 10 also).

Chapter 10
BACK TO THE FUTURE

The sea, oh the sea, is grá gheal mo chroí . . .
Thank God we're surrounded by water.

Recent popular Irish folk song.

NOW WE HAVE ALMOST COMPLETED our journey along the *boithrín na smaointe,* the memory lane, of Irish shellfisheries. Up ahead, we can perceive a fork in the road, but before that we can take a last backward glance at how we arrived where we are. It is at this juncture that we wish we had twenty-twenty binocular vision, that our foresight of things to come could match our hindsight of things past. But while we have figures and information to help focus our backward glance, our view ahead is not nearly as acute as we would like.

Throughout the twentieth century up to the 1960s the annual reported landings of molluscan shellfish varied from one to five thousand tonnes. They comprised native flat oysters and periwinkles almost exclusively and they were sold predominantly in the British market. From the late 1960s on, the trade expanded greatly so that total output by the end of the century was about 30,000 tonnes. (Exact values for molluscs are difficult to calculate since the statistics often refer only to generic "shellfish", that is, they include crustaceans like lobsters). The present day output comprises mussels, oysters (native and cupped), cockles, clams, scallops, whelks, razorfish and periwinkles. Shellfish harvesting and aquaculture provide employment to a significant number of people in both coastal and urban communities and Irish shellfish are now exported to over seventeen countries worldwide earning a total of over 43 million euro for the economy. The export value of all our aquaculture production, including salmon and trout, is about 80 million euro, so by any measure the humble shellfish are a vital component of the Irish seafood business and have attained an importance way beyond anything that might have been predicted at the start of that century.

In the 1950s and 1960s, a Breton family – the Oulhen family – dominated the shellfish trade, such as it was, on the west coast of Ireland. Their well-boat traversed the coast buying direct from the fishermen and transporting the fish – winkles, oysters, lobsters and salmon – direct to France or via their live storage tanks (Fig. 10) at Rock Island in Crookhaven Harbour (Fig. 78). When the boat was away, supplies were collected by truck and brought to Rock Island. The family business was eventually split into two companies, Primel (run by "Jean blanc") and Fruimar (run by "black Jean") that continued to trade until the 1980s. Knowledge of the biology, population structure and composition of the Irish shellfish stocks was poor at the time, fishermen were glad to have any buyers at all for their catch and there was no really strong indigenous seafood company in the west with good connections to the continental markets. At this remove it is hard to appreciate just how difficult it was to supply foreign markets with live shellfish before 1970, a time when there were no refrigerated trucks or "roll on roll off" ferries. The introduction of these latter two transport features did more than anything else to stimulate the expansion of the live shellfish trade from Ireland. Pádraic Mulloy of Mulloy's Seafoods in Westport recalls exporting winkles from Dublin in the 1950s. They were transported on the open decks of regular ferries with instructions to be hosed down with seawater at intervals. As often as not the instructions were overlooked, or the bags were hosed with water taken straight from the docks – hardly conducive to good quality control.

As mentioned already, it was Ireland's entry into the European Common Market that was the major demand-side catalyst for the burgeoning of the shellfish trade after 1970. But the supply-side catalyst was operating years earlier and it involved the contributions of a number of different agencies with radically different terms of reference. These were BIM, Gael Linn, the National Science Council (NSC) and University College Galway. BIM is a development body for the sea fisheries, providing finance, advice and technical support to the fishing industry. Gael Linn is a charitable trust dedicated to fostering and advancing the Irish language and Irish culture. Its then Chairman and Chief Executive, Dónal Ó Móráin, described as "a fanatic for the language but not a bigot" (a rare enough combination), was almost a one-man engine of development for the Irish-speaking areas (known as *an Ghaeltacht*) when those areas were receiving little official attention. The mantle of Gael Linn would eventually be taken on by

Gaeltarra Éireann and its successor, Údarás na Gaeltachta, official State development agencies for Gaeltacht affairs. The NSC, under its chairman Colm Ó hEocha, played a vital part in funding the very earliest scientific and environmental studies in aquaculture. It would later be transformed into the National Board for Science and Technology. Finally, University College Galway, a constituent college of the National University of Ireland, played an active and supportive role in the application of science to shellfish and the shellfisheries. Professor Pádraic Ó Céidigh, a long time advocate of the development of Ireland's marine resources, spearheaded the University's contribution.

Cooperation between agencies with such differing perspectives could hardly have been achieved without vision and compromise on all sides. Strangely enough, the disparate Agencies did succeed in cooperating and, with the financial help of the NSC, an embryonic plan was agreed that coordinated the emergence and development of Irish aquaculture. Such inter-agency cooperation is still altogether too rare in Irish public life. Its welcome occurrence in this instance was due in no small part to the vibrant interest and commitment of the main protagonists, Ó Móráin, Ó Céidigh and Ó hEocha, to the Irish language and culture and to the economic development of the Gaeltacht regions. Strangely too, the Fisheries Division of the Department of Agriculture, the State service charged with overseeing all aspects of the national fisheries, played only a minor role in promoting shellfish aquaculture. Certainly, one of its scientists, Colm Duggan, was active in developing the Tralee Bay and Clew Bay public oyster fisheries as well as in undertaking the preliminary experimental cultivation of American hard-shelled clams. Another, Michael Crowley, was actively researching mussels and had been involved in a preliminary, but unsuccessful, trial of raft culture at Cromane in the early 1960s. But Dr. Arthur E. J. Went, then Director of the Fisheries Division and Chief Fishery Adviser to the Minister, was not at all enthusiastic for aquaculture. He was only too aware of the legal niceties surrounding access to fish and fishing in tidal estuaries and in the sea and Went's worry was that these would prevent or seriously hinder any attempt to develop shellfish cultivation both on the foreshore and in shallow waters.

The public has a right to free fishing in tidal waters except where private fishing rights of very long standing (some say the rights must go back before year 1189) have been proved. From the mid-nineteenth century on, it was legislatively possible for the State to grant exclusive rights to parts of the sea and the shore for the purpose of oyster, mussel, cockle and winkle cultivation, but only in places not normally fished by the public. Naturally, the public would claim that all such suitable places had indeed been fished at some time or other in the past. The ancient law of free access therefore presented difficulties that various Ministers felt unable to resolve and that Went felt would grow even more intractable if strange new species were to be introduced. What, for instance, would happen if an exotic new species were introduced onto a derelict and abandoned public oyster bed? Could the public claim a right of fishery over a species that had never existed in Ireland previously? Or what would happen if strange new pathogens or parasites were introduced along with the exotic species? Could the public or the owners of adjacent beds claim damages if these spread disastrously? For these and other reasons, Went was not disposed to expend much of his own phenomenal energy and talents, or any of his staff, to promoting or advancing aquaculture. It fell to BIM therefore to take on the task of development. Looking back, it is difficult to appreciate just how daunting and demanding that task was at the time and just how deficient our support services were up to then.

BIM set up its Resource Development Section in 1967 to assess the status of the national shellfish stocks and to investigate the potential of aquaculture for their improvement. This was the first evaluation of the national public stocks of oysters, mussels and scallops ever undertaken and it set in train a process of local community involvement in the resource that is only now coming to full fruition. Making practical improvement in the public beds and their stocks proved to be very difficult for historical and sociological reasons, exactly as Went had foreseen. It is much to the credit of BIM and its staff that they persisted with their efforts despite the early setbacks. They eventually brought the public fisheries to a state where they are now amenable and responding to modern management techniques. In a number of cases, erstwhile private beds have been brought back into public ownership with great prospects for their rehabilitation. Their fate now lies largely with the local communities and "Went's worry" is less of a concern with them. As a State enterprise, BIM could only operate on the public fisheries; what happened with those private fisheries that remained private was a matter for their owners and in most cases they have continued in decline.

Dónal Ó Móráin and Gael Linn, with their sharper focus on the Irish language, faced a somewhat indirect task. The best way to foster the language, in Ó Móráin's view, was to support and encourage the people of the Gaeltacht to develop the indigenous natural resources of those regions. His aim was to restore the resources to a profitable and sustainable state so that the Irish-speaking communities could manage them for the common good. By improving the economic viability of the regions he hoped to slow the haemorrhage of young emigrants to more prosperous English-speaking areas in search of jobs. Among the enterprises he supported were the tweed industry and intensive pig farming along with other activities like music record production and a national lottery.

Fig. 79. Ancient Irish crest of the O'Meara family bearing eight scallops. Five Irish families have shells on their crest (the families Brehon, Graham, Reynolds and Tully are the others). In all cases the shell is a scallop shell. In heraldry a scallop shell most often signifies "travel" or "nautical prowess".

Oyster fishing, legal and illegal, was a long-established activity in the western Gaeltacht where some of the most productive and famous oyster beds were privately owned from time immemorial. The beds at Kilkieran Bay and Bertraghboy Bay (Bertraghboy in Irish is *Beirtreach buí*, meaning the yellow oyster bed) had once belonged to Richard (Humanity Dick) Martin of Ballinahinch Castle in Connemara. They passed from his family to the Berridge family who managed and developed them as best they could in the nineteenth century. By 1960 the beds were virtually derelict and in the possession of Ms. Lavelle, a member of the O'Meara family (Fig. 79) famous in Irish Nationalist circles in the early years of the State. She therefore received Ó Móráin generously and sympathetically when he approached her to buy the oyster rights to be held in trust on behalf of the people of the area. In due course the beds were vested in Gael Linn. Ó Móráin then approached the NSC and, in cooperation with the University, succeeded in obtaining financial support for a project to evaluate the status of the remaining oyster stocks in Connemara. The University was then in the course of building a Shellfish Research Laboratory at Carna (near Kilkieran) with the financial support of the Galway Regional Development Team and the NSC (Fig. 80).

There were relatively few trained shellfish biologists in Ireland in those days. The combined interests of Gael Linn, the National Science Council and the University provided the opportunity for this shortage to be addressed and rectified in a practical way. The Shellfish Research Laboratory was opened in 1973 and it engaged staff and students immediately. Michael Barry, a biologist then working with Hugh-Jones at Rossmore in Cork, was contracted by Gael Linn to undertake the Connemara oyster project and other students started research

Fig. 80. The Shellfish Research Laboratory, Carna, County Galway as it is today. This was the first great centre of modern Irish aquaculture research.

projects on the biology of the most important native shellfish species. They were Ireland's first generation of aquacultural experts to be trained at home.

Soon Ireland's shellfish development split into two separate strands. (In Ireland we are used to the idea of "the split" in all public affairs). Ó Móráin and some others wanted to develop the indigenous resources to be harvested on a sustainable, local scale. He had little time for hatcheries and artificial propagation. The University on the other hand, with its long-term basic science perspective, was more interested in following a clear scientific approach to shellfish biology (albeit of species of practical value) and especially in developing the new culture technologies that were then being studied in laboratories elsewhere. Both strands found a home in Carna, with Barry and others concentrating on the Connemara oyster beds and the University personnel concentrating on laboratory culture technology. Tony Whilde, who was developing the Clarinbridge oyster beds for BIM, also worked at the University's main campus where Pat Murray was doing the first-ever Irish Master's degree on suspended-culture of mussels.

Gaeltarra Eireann was watching with interest what was emerging at Carna but was limited by its remit to fostering only those enterprises that had clear commercial potential. It could not sponsor the University laboratory where scientific research was the prime objective and lack of funds the prime retardant. Therefore Gaeltarra set up a new Company, called Beirtreach Teoranta (Oysterbed Ltd.), whose remit was to commercialise shellfish culture in the Gaeltacht. Beirtreach erected a commercial oyster hatchery at Árd near Carna operating under the supervision of Damien O'Callaghan. Its other main activity was to identify potential sites in other Gaeltacht areas in which commercial shellfish cultivation might be undertaken and to set up trials in those areas. It sent its staff throughout the dispersed Gaeltacht in pursuit of these objectives. In this way, Beirtreach gave paid employment and much needed field experience to the new graduates emerging from the Shellfish Laboratory and from the Universities who, in time-honoured fashion, had boundless energy and enthusiasm but no money. The locations they identified as suitable would later become the main sites at which aquaculture would take root and flourish. They remain so to this day.

The ferment of administrative activity surrounding the birth of aquaculture and the interminable, marathon coordination meetings of the various sponsors went on apace. A doctor well known in shellfish circles recommended an effective prescription for lunch (see box, page 150) concocted precisely for such trying circumstances. He tells me that it worked wonders in facilitating the necessary cooperation that these meetings sought to achieve and contributed to the solving of many otherwise intractable problems.

From early on it became apparent that the hatchery technology was still only experimental and that Beirtreach was unlikely to meet its commercial goals in the immediate future. Everyone was learning that good research and development come before commercialisation. Gaeltarra responded by splitting Beirtreach (the "split" again!) into two separate entities – Taighde Mara Teo. (Sea Research Ltd.) that took over the site selection and other evaluation activities (together with many of the young staff) and Beirtreach Teo. itself, which retained the hatchery enterprise. Taighde Mara still continues in operation under Údarás na Gaeltachta serving the developmental and technological needs of the shellfish cultivation industry within and around the Gaeltacht.

A commercial operator involved in salmon farming eventually bought out the Beirtreach hatchery and broke its connection with shellfish. But another important lesson had been learnt all round: technical expertise and R&D were essential from the outset (the University's viewpoint), but without commercial viability, aquaculture was going nowhere (Gaeltarra's viewpoint). The young graduates who worked in the short-lived Beirtreach Teo. had been usefully exposed to the fundamental idea of economic viability without which no commercial venture could ever survive. As one of them, a biologist, remarked later, ". . . you soon learned how to draw up a business plan, something you had never heard of until then".

By the late 1970s, the Carna "campus" was becoming quite a centre for shellfish research and development. It provided a focus and an emergent centre of excellence where those interested in shellfish could gather and interact in a climate that encompassed both hatchery and wild stocks. Oysters, native and Pacific, were produced along with "new" species like the palourde and eventually the Manila clam. Later on, sea-urchins would be produced and Japanese abalone introduced and propagated. It was out from this campus that aquaculture exploded to *an Galltacht* (the English-speaking areas) where it added to the efforts of those who had been pioneering shellfish farming on their own or with BIM support. The "seed money" investment in the Gaeltacht region by Gael Linn, the NSC, University College Galway and Gaeltarra Eireann was to bear abundant fruit all over Ireland. One need only mention that the "Carna generation" included the likes of Damien O'Callaghan, James Ryan, John Wilson, Vincent Roantree, Kevin O'Kelly, Iarlaith Connellan, Cilian Roden, Bob Latouche, Tim Smith and many others to realise just how important that small campus was in the successful launch of fish and shellfish farming in Ireland. Most of the original *dramatis personae,* only some of whom we have mentioned, had left Carna by the late 1980s to take on roles in aquaculture at other locations. By then BIM was able to provide substantial financial assistance and administered EU support to new shellfish enterprises that now benefited from the availability of "home-grown" skilled and trained aquaculturists.

There were others too, like Niall Herriott, one of the first mussel farmers in the country, who contributed importantly to the advent of shellfish culture to Ireland. Michael Quinn in Tralee was tireless in endeavouring to develop the wild oyster fishery there and David Hugh-Jones battled against many odds in Rossmore to develop, expand and maintain that impressive venture. Séamas McQuaid pioneered the revival of the Carlingford Lough mussel fishery, driving his first bags of export mussels to the UK ferry piled in the boot and draped over the front wings of his ancient Simca car! Later on, he would export processed mussels canned in vinegar but this was discontinued when the cans exhibited a dangerous propensity to explode in transit! Unexplained explosions occurring in the Cooley Peninsula in the 1980s were much more risky for the unfortunate truck driver when stopped by a sceptical and understandably perplexed *Gárda,* than any potential hazard that the product might have presented to the culinary trade.

Many of the early pioneers are still active in one sector or another of what is now a mature industry whose origins seem strangely farther in the past than they really are. In Carna itself the Shellfish Laboratory continues to investigate the propagation of new species but at a very much reduced level. Today it is breeding such exotic fish as the sea horse and in its next phase it may become a centre for the cultivation of new marine finfish species. In retrospect, the industry seems to have got on to its feet quite quickly, some say just by following the practice in shellfish farming elsewhere, but also with considerable financial and innovative technical help from the University, BIM and latterly the Marine Institute. Aquaculture has gone from strength to strength since then, not without difficulties and setbacks. No boreen is entirely without its potholes and ruts but the shellfish industry is now a very, very long way indeed along the highway from the small localised harvesting industry of the pre-1960s era.

Inevitably, the ethos of the industry has changed as its scale increased: the emphasis is no longer on developing indigenous resources to an enhanced, sustainable level to be harvested by local communities. The focus has altered to the commercial production of enormous quantities of single species like mussels, or of imported species like cupped oysters or Manila clams, together with the pitiless harvesting of wild stocks of other indigenous species. What the future may hold we can try to predict, and here the feebleness of foresight may lead us into dangerous waters. The fork we can see in the road ahead is already clear: the artificial cultivation sector is now growing increasingly independent and going its own way separate from the harvesting sector, despite some "crossing-over", for example in the harvesting of wild seed mussels for cultivation elsewhere.

Hand harvesting of all species except winkles is rare now. Many of the traditional beds and species are fished out or reduced below commercially productive levels. Gross output is maintained in the harvesting sector largely by the relentless pursuit of new stocks and species, the expansion of harvesting into hitherto inaccessible sites and stocks and the use of mercilessly efficient dredging technology. The concept of sustainability, the idea of "harvesting within the capacity of the resource", has largely been lost sight of. Insatiable markets seem to demand that stocks must be immediately and rapaciously exploited to extinction with no thought for the future. Hydraulic fluidised-bed dredging leaves a churned-up sub-marine wasteland in its wake, literally as well as metaphorically, and only the most callous and shortsighted industry would encourage this kind of fishing. The seabed is home to many unassuming species without which the marine environment cannot function in a healthy way. All are stressed, if not actually killed or injured, by the passage of the hydraulic dredge and it takes up to forty days for the physical structure of the substrate to be re-established after it has passed. Ireland is not alone in adopting this technology. But its use elsewhere is hardly justification for its use here.

Even in cases where the harvesting method is less destructive of the environment it may be carried on at a scale that is simply not sustainable. The extraction of young seed mussels from the Irish Sea is a case in point. Just how long do we think the mussel stocks will survive if we continue to deplete them of the young recruits? Do we even know the origin of the Irish Sea seed? Just how long do we think that whelks, which have no planktonic dispersal phase, meaning that the number of recruits in any area depends critically on the adults of that area, will survive the current intensity of fishing? Why do we not see young razorfish on most beds? In the nineteenth century it was the orthodox view that the seas were inexhaustible. That view was held even as the wild oyster stocks of France, Holland, Ireland and Britain declined to virtual extinction. A repeat performance, this time with mussels, whelks and razorfish, is no longer just a remote possibility. It has already happened with clams and urchins in our day. It is time we listened to our own fishery scientists: unless we, along with them, can devise a national resource plan for the balanced cropping of our wild shellfish stocks (including crustacean species like lobsters, crayfish and crabs), the future looks gloomy. A return to localised, sustainable harvesting levels may be advisable in the short term. This is not an atavistic response to modern developments. It may, in fact, be the only safe future for marine resources that are already showing signs of serious over-exploitation. Perhaps quality – of product, of environment and of lifestyle – should come before quantity?

Even now, the sense of quality of lifestyle is an important issue that faces the industry. Already there is abundant evidence that young people are becoming reluctant to take up shellfish farming and fishing, preferring a lifestyle based on modern work (or play) practices and eschewing the demands associated with work at sea. The young always challenge us in this way and the manpower difficulty will be overcome in due course by increased mechanisation and advancing technology. Quality of product and quality of environment are quite other matters and will demand significant input from the landed as well as the coastal community.

If there is one idea that we have learned from shellfish farming it is the old one already well appreciated by viticulturists. It is the idea of *terroir*. That is the complex, almost indefinable, combination of geology, topography, soil, climate, weather, and general ambience of the local environment that give a wine its characteristic personality. Scientists might call it "micro-habitat" but that is not quite the whole idea. With shellfish, we have alluded to it already when we said that oysters take on the characteristics of the area in which they are grown and also when we mentioned that ropes suspended at the centre of a raft do not support mussels as well as those towards the edges. Aquatic *terroir* is as important to shellfish as terrestrial *terroir* is to the grape. Any shellfish grower will confirm that different sites, even different patches within a site, produce shellfish with different degrees of ease and of varying quality. The distribution of humps and hollows on a shore and the way they influence the tidal flow cause different parts to vary in their suitability as a home for shellfish. Every shore is really a patchwork of suitable sites rather than a uniform field for shellfish growth. This is also true with sub-tidal and suspended-culture sites and since the number of sites may be limited in some locations it can lead to conflict when site allocation is not managed carefully.

But it is the nature of bivalve shellfish themselves that has the greatest implications for quality matters. Because they are filter feeders they draw into their shell whatever may be dissolved or suspended in the water around them.

Much of what goes in must subsequently come out, but some of it stays inside for a greater or lesser period. In other words, bivalves can accumulate and concentrate substances that occur even at very low levels in the incoming water. If there are bacteria or viruses present, or chemical toxins or pollutants, they can "bio-accumulate" in the bivalves. That is why water quality is tested at all sites every two weeks and all water bodies are constantly being graded as to their hygienic suitability. The responsibility of ensuring that coastal waters are not degraded by the disposal of waste and sewage rests squarely with society in general. We are not, unfortunately, always as careful about this as we should be. All actions taken to ensure the highest water quality are to be commended, but as a community we have yet to embrace fully the discipline and determination that is needed if we are ever to improve the already depressed state of a great proportion of our coastal waters for shellfish or even for recreation. This is not just desirable, it is EU law. Shellfish can be the first organisms to signal that man-made degradation of the environment is taking hold so that the constant strict monitoring by the industry, the Marine Institute and BIM of our shellfish and the waters in which they grow is an important first line of defence for all of us in the matter of environmental quality. But will we respond appropriately and in time if they signal us that things are going downhill?

Not all of the hazards in the sea are man-made. Just as there are noxious weeds on land there are harmful, microscopic plants that occur naturally in the sea. One group of these is called the Dinoflagellates. In all European waters certain of these cause shellfish poisoning including the genera *Gonyaulax, Alexandrium, Pyrodinium, Pseudonitzschia* and *Prorocentrum*. These exotic names sound like the aliases of shadowy and surreptitious assassins, which in ways they are. They cause no symptoms in the shellfish but when humans consume affected shellfish they cause painful, debilitating and sometimes lethal poisoning. They are indigenous, natural planktonic residents of our seawater; blooms of them can explode naturally to give rise to "red tides" and tides of other colours too. Quite what triggers their sudden increase, or why they have become more frequent of late, is not known for certain but the upshot is certain: their occurrence will necessitate the immediate closure of all shellfish harvesting in the affected areas, which will remain closed until the "all-clear" is given. The time for them to clear away may be long in which case the growers may suffer great financial loss. Therefore a constant and effective watch for them is maintained at all times – whether a red tide is evident or not – to ensure that there is no hint of their presence in an area. Shellfish poisoning was once relatively common; the fact that we hear so little about it nowadays is testimony to the constancy and accuracy of our monitoring and the strictness of our regulations.

On balance, shellfish culture is not detrimental to the organisms that share their habitat with the cultured species or to the environment itself. John Harrington, who cultivates mussels and oysters in Kenmare Bay, sees a great increase in natural populations of shrimps near his enterprise and this may result from the increased food resource that detached mussels represent to the scavenging shrimp. Unless they are regularly cleaned, ropes and other structures in the water become rapidly colonized with sea squirts, barnacles, anemones and other settling organisms proving that cultivation does not affect adversely the diversity of animals in the locality. But where shellfish enterprises exist, size does matter. All of the animals in a bay depend ultimately on the plankton that comes into it. The filter feeders are the first to get at it, as it were. If there are too many filter-feeding mouths to be fed in the farms then all of the goodness can be filtered out of the water before the natural, sedentary wild organisms get their chance to feed. The consequences that inevitably flow from this do not need to be spelt out. Sometimes the effect will become obvious as a drop in production in the farm, or on a natural bed, furthest away from the new, incoming seawater. This is happening in many bays in France and already in Ireland there are indications that we may be approaching capacity saturation in some areas. When that occurs aquaculture is patently excessive and a reduction in cultivated stock size is called for. Unless we anticipate such problems and manage the extent of aquaculture in good time it is the wild organisms that will suffer first, most and in silence. That is, we will not realize the wild fauna is suffering until it is already well reduced.

All these issues emphasize that the shellfish growing and harvesting activities of a bay are closely interrelated and have influence on the other residents of the water and the sea bottom. The totality of activities in an area including aquacultural, recreational, domestic and tourist, should do no damage to the high natural quality of the water. Put differently, each activity in a locality affects every other activity and the pursuit of one must not cause deterioration in any other. To ensure this, Ireland is to the forefront in advancing schemes of Single Bay Management and Coordinated Local Aquaculture Management (CLAMS). The latest scheme, ECOPACT, is a strategy launched by BIM and the aquaculture industry to foster the universal use of environmental management systems in the industry. In all of these schemes, the local users cooperate to develop viable management plans for their locality with the help of the State agencies. Such plans balance the needs of the various interests, including the wild fauna and flora, to optimize the benefit to the community of the important public resource that the sea represents. Results of CLAMS efforts are now evident at many sites: the visual and environmental impacts of aquaculture and other aquatic activities are being reduced, equitable and sustainable sharing is being advanced, financial benefits to the locality are being enhanced and the sense of community ownership of the water resource is taking hold again among ordinary people. The schemes are, in a sense, taking back the resource as the patrimony of the nation for the enrichment of the community, just like it was long ago when families enhanced their diet with "kitchen" and sometimes their pockets with "eister money". We may indeed be going back to the future. *Ar aghaidh linn, agus go n-éirigh ár saothar linn!*

Prescription for "lunch all in a shell"

FOR FIVE PERSONS

5 X one dozen best native flat oysters;
5 X half pint of Guinness in one pint glasses;
1 X bottle of champagne.
Top up the Guinness with the champagne.
Enjoy!
Repeat as necessary.

ACKNOWLEDGMENTS

IT WAS TOMÁS BURKE of BIM who first suggested that I write a book on Irish shellfish. By the time I realised just how few written records were available to research, it was too late to change my mind. Both Tomás and Mícheál Ó Cinnéide of the Marine Institute were already advancing names of contacts and otherwise encouraging me to stick with the task. Pat Keogh of BIM was also immensely encouraging from the very beginning. This book may not be quite what they had anticipated but their keen interest in modern Irish shellfish and in the traditions of the Irish coastal communities makes me hope that they are not entirely disappointed. Their constant support is greatly appreciated and without them this book would never have materialised.

The paucity of comprehensive written records meant that facts and stories had to be gleaned piecemeal from whatever sources could be come by and the total had then to be formed into a coherent whole. It could ever only be a gathering, a *cnuasach,* or in the language of food, a *plateau de fruits de mer,* depending for its effect on how well it is presented. The readers will decide for themselves whether or not it is a dish worth sampling. Those who contributed ingredients include Michael Barry, Duncan Brown, Leo Boyle, John Chamberlain, Tim Coakley, Mícheál Corduff, Eddie Fahy, Michael Gibbons, Mary Hannan, John Harrington, Jim Harty, Pat and Mary Holland, David Hugh-Jones, Tom Keenan, Des Lett, Criostóir MacCárthaigh, Nollaig McConghaile, Terry McCoy, Mattie McInerney Jnr., Seamas McQuaid, Tom Mitchell, Andy Mulloy, Padraic Mulloy, Kevin O'Kelly, Brian O'Loan, Danny O'Sullivan, Pat and Mary Power, Diarmuid Ring, Seán Ryan, John Slater and Damien Toner. If I have messed up the good ingredients they generously contributed, the fault is mine alone. Any opinions expressed are entirely my own sauce and do not necessarily represent the positions or views of my correspondents or sponsors who made no attempt to sway me to any particular view or opinion.

Tomás Burke, Richie Flynn, Ian Lawler, Carmel Lynn, Mícheál Ó Cinnéide and Vera O'Donovan gave invaluable help with contacts. My colleague Eoin MacLoughlin was knowledgeable and helpful in many aspects of the work and he read early drafts with patience and with helpful comments. Des Kenny advised on publishing matters and Brendan Wilkins advised on digital photography and computing. At the end, before the dish was finally brought to the table, Tomás Burke, Henry Comerford, Eoin MacLoughlin, Criostóir MacCárthaigh, Cilian Roden, Mícheál Ó Cinnéide and Mícheál Corduff read it. I am grateful to them for their comments and valuable advice.

Brian O'Loan provided the photographs reproduced as figures 68 and 69. David Hugh-Jones provided figure 62, Eric Edwards provided figure 56 and Marianne Whilde provided figures 19, 55 and 60. I thank Darina Allen and Terry McCoy for providing recipes and Hamlyn Publishers for the extract from *Nouveau Larousse Gastronomique*. Figure 12 is reproduced, with permission, from *Crustaceana* (E. J. Brill, Leiden).

There are others, including many shellfish farmers and members of the Irish Shellfish Association, whom I have unintentionally omitted to name whose knowledge and advice have gone into the mix quietly but effectively. I thank all of them for their assistance.

Finally, my thanks to Anne Korff of Tír Eolas for her wonderful illustrations and her enthusiasm in publishing this and to my sponsors, BIM, the Marine Institute and Údarás na Gaeltachta for their generous, unencumbered support. *Rath éisc oraibh!*

SOURCES

THERE IS NO SINGLE BOOK about Irish shellfish and shellfisheries. References to various shellfish and related matters will be found in the publications below. For detailed information readers are referred to *Squires Spalpeens and Spats: Oysters and Oystering in Galway Bay* and *Ponds, Passes and Parcs: Aquaculture in Victorian Ireland* referenced below in which more extensive treatment and references are given.

Becker, H. *I mBéal na Farraige*. Indreabhán, Cló Iar-Chonnachta, 1997. Translated by the author as *Seaweed Memories. In the Jaws of the Sea*. Dublin, Wolfhound Press, 2000. ISBN 0 86327 835 3.

Bórd Iascaigh Mhara. Various issues of *Fish Farming Newsletter* and *Aquaculture*, newsletters produced in support of the aquaculture industry.

Boudry, P. *et al.* Differentiation between populations of the Portuguese oyster, *Crassostrea angulata* and the Pacific oyster *Crassostrea gigas* (Thunberg) revealed by mtDNA RFLT analysis. Journal of Experimental Marine Biology and Ecology, 226, 279 – 291, 1998.

Breathnach, C. *A Word in your Ear. Folklore from the Kinara area*. Kinvara, Comhairle Phobail Chinn Mhara, no date (c 2000).

Commission into the Methods of Oyster Culture. Report to the Houses of Parliament. [C-224]. Dublin, Alex Thom, 1870.

Commissioners of Inquiry into the State of the Irish Fisheries. First Report. Dublin, Alex Thom, 1836.

Collins, T. Oysters and Antiquities: a Biographical Note on E. W. L. Holt. Journal of the Galway Archaeological and Historical Society, vol. 43, 158 – 166.

Cork Weekly Examiner, The. The Cromane Mussel Fishery. 26 Feb, 1960.

Cox, I. (Editor) The *Scallop. Studies of a shell and its influences on Humankind.* London, Shell Transport and Trading Company, 1957.

Crowley, M. Making more Money from Periwinkles. Department of Agriculture and Fisheries Ireland, Fisheries Leaflet No. 74, 1975.

Evans, E. E. *Mourne Country. Landscapes and Life in South Down*. Dundalk, Dundalgan Press, N.D.

Evans, E. E. *Irish Folk Ways*. London, Routledge and Kegan Paul, 7th impression, 1979.

Evans, E. E. *Irish Heritage. The Landscape, the People and their Work*. Dundalk, Dundalgan Press, 1942.

Fahy, E. *et al.* Distribution, Population Structure, Growth and Reproduction of the Razor Clam *Ensis arcuatus* (Jeffrreys) (Solenaceae) in Coastal Waters of Western Ireland. Irish Fisheries Investigations No.10, 2001.

Fishery Commissioners, Ireland. Reports. 1853 to 1865. Dublin, Alex Thom, 1854 to 1866.

Gibson, F. A. Notes on the Escallop (*Pecten maximus* L.) in three closely associated Bays in the West of Ireland. Journal du Conseil International pour l'Exploration de la Mer, 24, No.2, 366 – 371, 1959.

Gibson, F. A. Escallops (*Pecten maximus L.*) in Irish Waters. Scientific Proceedings of the Royal Dublin Society, 27, No.8, 253 – 271, 1956.

Irish Skipper, The. Most issues of this important fisheries newspaper contain articles and news on shellfish and aquaculture topics. Dundrum, Dublin, Mac Communications.

Latouche, B., K. Moylan and W. Twomey, 1993. *Abalone On-growing Manual*. Aquaculture Explained No. 14. Dublin, An Bórd Iascaigh Mhara, 1993.

Lewes, G. H. *Seaside Studies*. London, William Blackwood, 1860.

Local Government Board for Ireland. Report on the shellfish Layings on the Coast of Ireland. (T. J. Browne). Dublin, HMSO, 1904. [Cd 1900].

Mac an Iomaire, S. *Cladaigh Chonamara*. Dublin, An Gúm, 1938. Translated by P. de Bhaldraithe as *The Shores of Connemara*. Kinvara, Tír Eolas Publishers, 2000. ISBN 1 873821 14 X

Maxwell, W. H. *Wild Sports of the West*. Dublin, Talbot Press, N.D.

McCormick, F., Gibbons, M., McCormack, F. G. and Moore, J. Bronze Age to Medieval Coastal Shell Middens near Ballyconneely, Co. Galway. The Journal of Irish Archaeology, VII, 77 – 84, 1996.

Minchin, D. The Escallop *Pecten maximus* (L.) in Mulroy Bay. Irish Fisheries Research Report No. 1, 1981.

Murphy, Sean. The mystery of Molly Malone. Dublin, Divelina Publications, 1992. ISBN 0951261126

ÓhEochaidh, S. Seanchas Iascaireachta agus Farraige. In *Bealoideas*, edited by S. Ó'Duilearga, Vol.33, 1 – 96, 1965.

Partridge, J. K. *Studies on Tapes decussatus (L) in Ireland*. Ph.D. thesis, National University of Ireland, University College Galway 1977.

Praeger, R. L. *The Way that I Went. An Irishman in Ireland*. Dublin, Hodges, Figgis and Co., 1937.

Philpots, J. R. *Oysters and All about Them*. 2 vols. London, John Richardson and Co., 1891.

Tattersall, W.M. Notes on the Breeding Habits and Life History of the Periwinkle. Scientific Investigations of the Department of Agriculture and Technical Instruction for Ireland, 1920, No. 1, 1920.

Thompson, W. *The Natural History of Ireland*. Vol 4. London, H. G. Bohn, 1856.

Verling, Máirtín (Editor). *Béarrach Mná ag caint*. Indreabhán, Cló Iar-Chonnachta, 1999.

Walne, P.R. *Culture of Bivalve Molluscs. 50 years experience at Conwy*. West Byfleet, Fishing News Books Ltd., 1974. ISBN 0 85238 063

Went, A. E. J. Historical Notes on the Oyster Fisheries of Ireland. Proceedings of the Royal Irish Academy 62, C7, 195 – 223, 1962.

Went, A. E. J. Mariculture in Ireland Policies and Problems. Department of Agriculture and Fisheries Ireland, Fisheries Leaflet No.73, 1975.

Wilkins, N. P. *Ponds, Passes and Parcs. Aquaculture in Victorian Ireland*. Dublin, The Glendale Press, 1989. ISBN 0 907606 65 2

Wilkins, N. P. *Squires Spalpeens and Spats, Oysters and Oystering in Galway Bay*. Galway, the Author, 2001. ISBN 0 9540523 0 7

INDEX *Numbers in* **bold** *refer to illustrations.*

Tír Eolas is a small independent publishing house based in Doorus near Kinvara, Co. Galway. Since its first publication in 1985, *Kinvara, a Rambler's Guide and Map*, the company has continued to produce high quality books, guides and maps that provide information on Irish history, landscape, culture and tradition.

Tír Eolas has published seven **Guides and Maps**, covering the Burren, South Galway, Kinvara, Medieval Galway and Loch Corrib. They give detailed information on the archaeological and historical sites, the birds, animals and flowers to be seen and the natural features found in the area covered by each map. They are the ideal aid to the discovery and exploration of the Burren and South Galway.

Books from Tír Eolas

The Shores of Connemara, by Séamus Mac an Iomaire, translated by Pádraic de Bhaldraithe, 2000. A naturalist's guide to the seashore and coastal waters of Connemara, Co. Galway and an account of the life of the people who lived there in the late nineteenth and early twentieth century.
ISBN 1-873821-14-X PB

A Burren Journal, by Sarah Poyntz, 2000. Sarah Poyntz's diaries give a striking picture of life in the unique landscape of the Burren. She describes the changing seasons, the birds and animals, the wild flowers for which the Burren is famous and the lives of the people of the village of Ballyvaughan. The illustrations by Anne Korff and Gordon D'Arcy bring her words to life.
ISBN 1-873821-13-1 PB

The Book of the Burren, edited by Jeff O'Connell and Anne Korff, 1991. An introduction to the geology, natural history, archaeology and history of the Burren region. 2nd edition 2002.
ISBN 1-873821-15-8 PB

The Book of Aran, edited by John Waddell, Jeff O'Connell and Anne Korff, 1994. An introduction to the natural history, archaeology, history, folklore and literary heritage of the Aran Islands.
ISBN 1-873821-03-4 PB

Kinvara, a Seaport Town on Galway Bay, written by Caoilte Breatnach and compiled by Anne Korff, 1997. Social history and folklore seen through photographs.
ISBN 1-873821-07-7 PB

Women of Ireland, by Kit and Cyril Ó Céirín, 1996.
A biographical dictionary of Irish women from earliest times to the present. It documents the rich and varied contributions women have made to the shaping of Irish history and culture.
ISBN 1-873821-06-9 PB

The Shannon Floodlands, by Stephen Heery, 1993.
A natural history of the callows, the distinctive landscape seasonally flooded by the River Shannon.
ISBN 1-873821-02-6 PB

Not a Word of a Lie, by Bridie Quinn-Conroy, 1993.
A portrait of growing up in a small community in the West of Ireland.
ISBN 1-873821-01-8 PB